PALAEOLITHIC ARCHAEOLOGY OF THE SOLENT RIVER

Proceedings of the Lithic Studies Society day meeting held at the Department of
Archaeology, University of Southampton on Saturday 15th January 2000

Edited by

F.F. Wenban-Smith & R.T. Hosfield

Lithic Studies Society Occasional Paper No. 7 (2001)

Published by
Lithic Studies Society
c/o British Museum (Quaternary Section)
Franks House, 38–46 Orsman Road
London, N1 5QJ

Printed and bound by
Cambrian Printers
Aberystwyth

ISBN   0-9513246-3-2
ISSN   0950 - 9208

British Library Cataloguing in Publication Data
A catalogue record of this book is available from the British Library

Front cover
False colour composite satellite image of the Solent region from Landsat Thematic Mapper, processed
by the Geodata Unit, University of Southampton (courtesy of Prof. M. Clark and Chris Hill)

PREFACE AND ACKNOWLEDGEMENTS

In many ways Frances Healy is to thank for the fact that the meeting on which this volume is based took place. A casual conversation with one of the organisers (FFW-S) on some curious typological characteristics in the Southampton terraces, and the low profile of the Solent region despite the plethora of material, culminated in the suggestion "wouldn't that make a good subject for a Lithic Studies Society meeting?". The Department of Archaeology at the University of Southampton seemed the obvious base for such a meeting, and FFW-S would like to thank the embryonic Centre for the Archaeology of Human Origins (CAHO) for agreeing to host the meeting, and to express particular gratitude to RTH for agreeing to co-organise the meeting, for his contribution and enthusiasm in helping to set the meeting up and ensure its smooth running, and for his huge input subsequently into the task of editing the papers for this volume. RTH would like to thank FFW-S for all his hard work in developing Frances Healy's initial idea and in attracting many of the current heavyweights in British Palaeolithic studies.

We would both also like to thank Professor David Peacock and the Department of Archaeology for providing space and facilities for the meeting to take place and covering the travel expenses of some of the contributors, and the security staff for ensuring there was no problem with out-of-hours access. Finally, and most importantly, we are also grateful to all those who devoted a precious weekend to either speaking at or attending the meeting, which helped to make it, on general agreement of those who participated, such a success.

On an editorial note, we decided that, to retain as much as possible of the freshness and tone of the original meeting, we would adopt the lightest possible editorial hand for contributors. Thus any changes of opinion or new developments thrown up in the course of the meeting are not necessarily reflected in these published papers, which follow as far as possible the original presentations, and we have allowed contributors to speak in their own distinctive voices, without any editorial interference. Given the futility of attempting to please all of the people all of the time, we hope that the consequent diversity of tone may at least please all of the people some of the time.

Francis Wenban-Smith and Robert Hosfield, 10th July 2001.

TABLE OF CONTENTS

List of figures   v

List of tables   vi

List of contributors   vii

1. Introduction   1
    F.F. Wenban-Smith
2. The Geology of the Solent River System   7
    J.K. Dix
3. The Pleistocene evolution and Palaeolithic occupation of the Solent River   15
    D.R. Bridgland
4. The meeting of the waters: raised beaches and river gravels of the Sussex Coastal
    Plain/Hampshire Basin   27
    M.R. Bates
5. Some Earlier Palaeolithic find-spots of interest in the Solent region   47
    D.A. Roe
6. As represented by the Solent River: handaxes from Highfield, Southampton   57
    F.F. Wenban-Smith
7. Priory Bay, Isle of Wight: a review of current knowledge   71
    R.D. Loader
8. The Broom pits: a review of research and a pilot study of two Acheulian biface
    assemblages   77
    G.D. Marshall
9. The Lower Palaeolithic of the Solent: 'site' formation and interpretive frameworks   85
    R.T. Hosfield
10. Prospecting the Palaeolithic: strategies for the archaeological investigation of Middle
    Pleistocene deposits in Southern England   99
    K. Wilkinson

Site and Find-spot Index   111

LIST OF FIGURES

1.1: topography and drainage of the Hampshire/Solent River Basin 2

1.2: Pleistocene geology of the Solent region 3

1.3: Palaeolithic find-spots around Bournemouth 4

2.1: Solid geology of the middle and lower reaches of the Solent River system 8

3.1: the Solent River drainage system 16

3.2: map of the terrace gravels of the Solent River between Poole and Fawley 17

3.3: long profiles of the Solent and Frome terrace surfaces 18

3.4: idealized transverse section through the Solent terrace staircase 19

3.5: map of the last glacial English Channel River system 20

3.6: the pre-Holocene Solent River system 21

3.7: formation of river terraces in synchrony with Quaternary climate change 22

4.1: site location plan for the West Sussex Coastal Plain 28

4.2: schematic profile of the West Sussex Coastal Plain raised beach sequence 30

4.3: the distribution of the major gravel bodies of the Solent and Southampton districts 32

4.4: major river valleys and their offshore equivalents within the West Sussex Coastal Plain 34

4.5: the relationship between climate systems, uplift and the nature of sediment deposition at the mouth of major river valleys entering the West Sussex Coastal Plain area 36

4.6: location of sediment units and mapped terraces in the Portsdown–Portsmouth corridor 37

4.7: cross-profiles through key sites in the Portsdown area, Hampshire 38

4.8: distribution of sediment units at the mouth of the river Arun 40

5.1: handaxes from Corfe Mullen 50

5.2: handaxes from Warren Hill 51

5.3: handaxes from Test Road Materials Pit, Romsey 52

5.4: pointed plano-convex handaxes from the Wolvercote Channel, Oxford 53

5.5: pointed plano-convex handaxes from the Wolvercote Channel, Oxford 54

6.1: quarrying locations A–D in Highfield and Pleistocene terraces 62

6.2: handaxes from Highfield Church Pit 64

6.3: variety of handaxes from Highfield 65

6.4: pointed handaxes on unifacially worked side-struck flakes 66

7.1: Isle of Wight Palaeolithic find-spots 72

7.2: the location of Priory Bay and the 1986 excavation 73

7.3: a selection of handaxes recovered from the beach at Priory Bay 74

7.4: section excavated at the top of the cliff at Priory Bay in 1986 75

7.5: implement found *in situ* during the excavation of 1986 76

8.1: rolling and shape for Charles Bean's Holditch Lane biface collection 79

8.2: edge profile and rolling amongst the Old Ballast Pit collection 80

8.3: blank form and rolling amongst the Old Ballast Pit collection 80

8.4: butt working and rolling for fresh and rolled bifaces from the Old Ballast Pit collection 81

8.5: working intensity cumulative frequency histogram for fresh and rolled bifaces from the Old Ballast Pit collection 81

8.6: weight cumulative frequency histogram for fresh and rolled bifaces from the Old Ballast Pit collection 81

8.7: shape diagrams for fresh and rolled bifaces from the Old Ballast pit collection 82

9.1: spatio-temporal origins of secondary context, river gravel find-spots 86

9.2: Location of Wood Green and Dunbridge in the Solent Basin 86

9.3: Section at Wood Green 87

9.4: Section at Dunbridge 88

9.5: model of regional archaeological structure 89

9.6: abrasion of handaxe samples from Wood Green and Dunbridge 91

9.7: model of river rejuvenation and terrace preservation on Tertiary bedrock 91

9.8: model of river rejuvenation and terrace preservation on Chalk bedrock 91

9.9: Bridgland's 5-phase cyclical climatic model of river terrace formation 92

9.10: pre-Quaternary geology of the Solent Basin and three Lower Palaeolithic find-spots 93

9.11: modelled distribution of handaxes along the River Test valley 94

9.12: modelled handaxe densities in the River Test catchment by glacial/interglacial cycle   95
9.13: models of Middle Pleistocene hominid occupation of the Solent Basin   96
10.1: location of sites referred to in the text and the southern margins of Devensian glacier ice   101
10.2: West Sussex Coastal Plain raised beach sequence   105
10.3: Bridgland's model of fluvial terrace development over a single glacial/interglacial cycle   106

LIST OF TABLES

4.1: chronostratigraphy and lithostratigraphy of the main sequences in the West Sussex Coastal Plain   31
4.2: lithostratigraphic units of the Solent River system   33
4.3: lithostratigraphic correlation chart for the West Sussex Coastal Plain/Hampshire Basin corridor   42
6.1: condition of Highfield handaxes   63
6.2: types of Highfield handaxes   67
8.1: suggested rolling categories and those defined by Charles Bean for the Holditch Lane collection   79
8.2: suggested shape categories and those defined by Charles Bean for the Holditch Lane collection   79
8.3: rolling and shape categories based on Charles Bean's analysis of the Holditch Lane bifaces   79
8.4: attributes listed for the Old Ballast Pit collection   80
9.1: Palaeolithic artefacts from Wood Green, Dunbridge and Kimbridge   87
10.1: English Heritage criteria for identifying 'value' in the English Palaeolithic   104

LIST OF CONTRIBUTORS

M. R. Bates

Department of Archaeology, University of Wales, Lampeter, Ceredigion, SA48 7ED, UK. E-mail: m.bates@lamp.ac.uk

D. R. Bridgland

Department of Geography, University of Durham, Science Site, South Road, Durham, DH1 3LE, UK. E-mail: D.R.Bridgland@durham.ac.uk

J. K. Dix

Centre for Maritime Archaeology, Department of Archaeology, University of Southampton, Avenue Campus, Highfield, Southampton, SO17 1BJ, UK. E-mail: j.dix@soc.soton.ac.uk

R. T. Hosfield

Centre for the Archaeology of Human Origins (CAHO), Department of Archaeology, University of Southampton, Avenue Campus, Highfield, Southampton, SO17 1BJ, UK. E-mail: rth1@soton.ac.uk

R. D. Loader

Isle of Wight County Archaeology and Historic Environment Service, County Archaeological Centre, 61 Clatterford Road, Newport, Isle of Wight, PO30 1NZ, UK. E-mail: rebecca.loader@iow.gov.uk

G. D. Marshall

Centre for the Archaeology of Human Origins (CAHO), Department of Archaeology, University of Southampton, Avenue Campus, Highfield, Southampton, SO17 1BJ, UK. E-mail: gilbert@soton.ac.uk

D. A. Roe

Donald Baden-Powell Quaternary Research Centre, Oxford University, 60 Banbury Road, Oxford, OX2 6PN, UK. E-mail: derek.roe@pitt-rivers-museum.oxford.ac.uk

F. F. Wenban-Smith

Centre for the Archaeology of Human Origins (CAHO), Department of Archaeology, University of Southampton, Avenue Campus, Highfield, Southampton, SO17 1BJ, UK. E-mail: ffws@soton.ac.uk

K. Wilkinson

Department of Archaeology, King Alfred's College, Winchester, SO22 4NR, UK. E-mail: K.Wilkinson@wkac.ac.uk

1. INTRODUCTION

F.F. Wenban-Smith

BACKGROUND

The papers in this volume originated as a series of presentations for the Lithic Studies Society day meeting *Palaeolithic Archaeology of the Solent River* held on 15 January 2000, and hosted by the Centre for the Archaeology of Human Origins (CAHO) in the Department of Archaeology, University of Southampton. The germ of the meeting came from a small investigation into the collections of Palaeolithic material from terraces in the Highfield area of Southampton (Chapter 6). This investigation highlighted the distinctive nature of at least some material from the Solent region, and suggested it was high time more attention was focused upon studying the prolific evidence from this relatively neglected region, which, along with East Anglia and the Thames Valley, is one of the three main areas in Britain where surviving Palaeolithic evidence is concentrated (cf. Roe 1981: 132–3).

At the same time, a number of workers had recently finished or were starting doctoral research into different aspects of the Palaeolithic of the Solent region. Hosfield (1999) had investigated the potential of the predominantly derived Palaeolithic material of the region to investigate demographic trends and landscape exploitation strategies at a macro scale, based on modelling artefact densities in terrace gravel units at broad temporal resolutions. Chambers was starting to investigate the taphonomy of the Palaeolithic archaeological collections from the region. And finally, at the instigation of Hampshire County Council's Archaeology Section, Terry was starting to work on modelling the Palaeolithic archaeological potential of Pleistocene deposits in Hampshire, in an attempt to identify, and most importantly predict, the location of those of highest potential (cf. Wilkinson, Chapter 10).

Alongside this groundswell of renewed archaeological interest, a number of Quaternary geological investigations had also recently taken place. The Southampton area was chosen in the early 1980s for a case study into the potential of geological mapping to feed into the land-use and strategic development planning functions of local government (Edwards *et al.* 1987). One of the many useful products of this project was revised BGS mapping of the Quaternary deposits of the area, and the recognition of 14 distinct fluvial terrace formations (Edwards & Freshney 1987), three of them

submerged under the Solent (Dyer 1975). This was complemented by revised BGS mapping of the Quaternary of the Bournemouth area, where Bristow *et al.* (1991) also identified 14 terraces, and the work of Allen & Gibbard (1993) who identified 19 separate terrace units along the south coast between Bournemouth and Southampton Water. Unfortunately no overlap was made between these units and the terrace sequences established by the BGS, leading to detailed adjacent local sequences with uncertain correlation (cf. Wymer 1999: 108, Table 9).

An added complication is the general lack of biological evidence in the Pleistocene deposits of the Solent region, leading to problems in chronometric dating and in establishing correlations between the terrace sequences of different river valleys within the region, and of these terrace sequences with the wider Thames lithostratigraphic sequence and the global Oxygen Isotope framework. Meanwhile, to the east of Southampton, the sequence of Quaternary raised beach and associated deposits of the Sussex coastal plain had also recently been studied by Bates *et al.* (1997). As pointed out by Bates *et al.*, in a theme taken up in this volume (Chapter 4), the best hope for dating the Solent sequences may lie in establishing direct lithostratigraphic relationships of the Solent formations with the better dated Sussex deposits where the deposits of these two regions overlap in the Portsmouth area.

Given this background of freshly completed and ongoing work in the region, the main purpose of the meeting was to bring together Palaeolithic archaeologists and Quaternary geologists working in the region to discuss the implications, and possible beneficial cross-fertilisations, for each other of this research, and to share the preliminary results of work in progress. It was also an opportunity to review the range of focus of current Palaeolithic archaeology and to highlight to the local curatorial community both the diverse nature of significant Palaeolithic evidence and the integral role in Palaeolithic archaeological research of Quaternary studies. For many in a curatorial role, Palaeolithic archaeology is an esoteric discipline with rapidly changing theoretical perspectives brought to bear in its study. This, together with the natural geological context of the unimpressive (to some!) bits of stone which are its bread and butter, and the tenuous chains of thought by which this evidence is transformed into knowledge, makes it hard for many

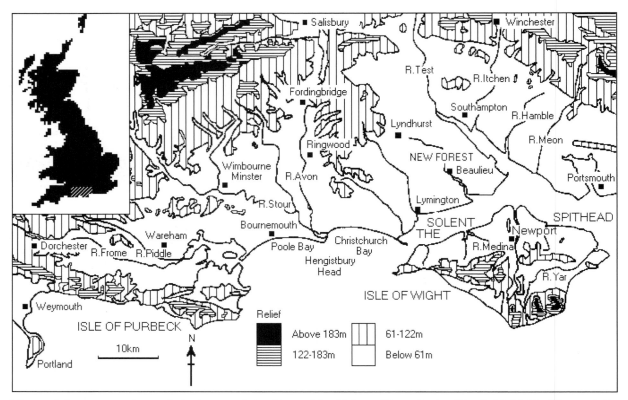

Figure 1.1: topography and drainage of the Hampshire/Solent River Basin (Hosfield 1999: Figure 2.9, after Allen & Gibbard 1993)

curators to bring the full weight of the planning mechanism to bear on protecting the Palaeolithic archaeological resource and mitigating the impact of development. If the needs of the Palaeolithic heritage are to be met under the framework of PPG 16 (Department of the Environment 1990; Wenban-Smith 1995), it is incumbent upon those actively working in this specialised area to engage proactively with curators, and to explain the nature and potential of the Palaeolithic archaeological resource, to help bring the Palaeolithic on board as part of the cultural heritage, on a par with any Neolithic henge or Roman villa.

If one had to select just one key issue that arose from the meeting, it would be the problem of establishing dates and correlations for the proven artefact-rich Pleistocene deposits of the Solent region. Palaeolithic archaeology is a human historical discipline, and accurate dating is essential to document events in relation to each other to allow the building up of a picture of the degree and spatial scale of contemporary variability, and the trajectories of cultural stasis and change through the changing climatic framework of the Pleistocene. As mapping and lithostratigraphic correlations of depositional units become more detailed, accurate dating of even a few key units can provide foundations to tie in the whole sequence, and its contained archaeological horizons, with the wider national and international frameworks. This dating will most likely be achieved from the study

of biological evidence — pollen, large vertebrates, molluscs or small vertebrates — from archaeologically sterile Pleistocene deposits. Thus a central aspect of the Palaeolithic archaeological agenda in the region has to be the discovery and study of such deposits, for they surely exist somewhere beyond the very few locations where biological evidence has already been reported. It is to be hoped that the curatorial community in the Solent region can follow the lead set in other regions such as Kent, Essex and Greater London in recognising that such deposits are an integral part of the archaeological record, and worthy of protection or mitigation under the current planning control mechanisms.

THE SOLENT RIVER REGION

The Solent River no longer exists, but through the majority of the Pleistocene was the main river draining the Hampshire Basin (Figure 1.1), which consists of a synclinal depression in the Cretaceous Chalk filled in its central part with Tertiary deposits, with a predominantly east-west long axis dipping slightly to the east. Chalk capped with Clay-with-flints outcrops on the high ground around the edge of the basin, forming the Wiltshire Downs, the North Dorset Downs, the Hampshire Downs and the Isle of Wight Downs. This basin is drained by a series of small rivers with

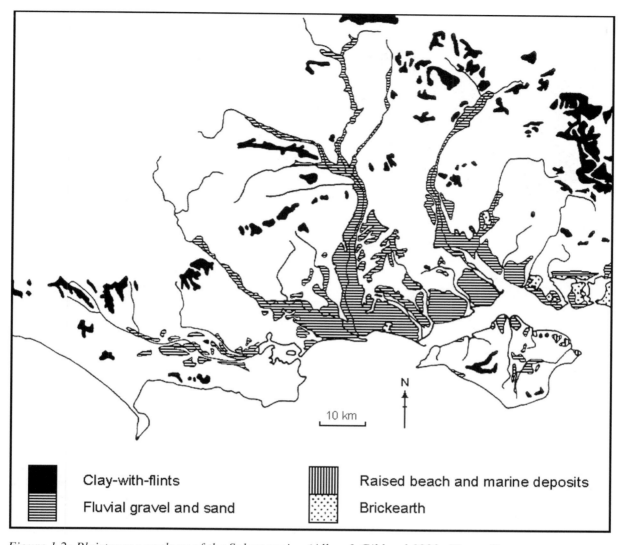

Figure 1.2: Pleistocene geology of the Solent region (Allen & Gibbard 1993: Figure 3)

their headwaters in the surrounding Chalk downland, in particular the Frome, Piddle, Wiltshire Stour, Wiltshire Avon, Test and Itchen on the mainland, and, on the Isle of Wight, the Medina and the Yar. The mainland rivers drain directly into the Channel in the present-day, due to the breaching of the southern Chalk ridge of the Hampshire basin between Durlston Head and The Needles, and those on the Isle of Wight drain north into the Solent. Through much of the Pleistocene, however, they would have fed a major east-west river, christened the Solent River by Fox (1862), the headwaters of which coincided with the present-day River Frome, and which would have passed through Poole Harbour and the West and East Solent to the north of the Isle of Wight, before heading south to join the English Channel.

The Hampshire basin contains extensive spreads of Pleistocene fluvial deposits relating to the evolution of its drainage through the period, concentrated in the valleys of the current rivers Frome, Stour, Avon and Test, and in a great swathe along the south coast

between Bournemouth and Southampton Water (Figure 1.2). Pleistocene raised beach deposits have also been identified in the eastern part of the region, near Fareham on the mainland (ApSimon *et al.* 1977), and at Bembridge and Priory Bay at the eastern tip of the Isle of Wight (Preece *et al.* 1990; Bridgland 1999). The study and interpretation of these deposits has been complicated by several factors including their proximity to the coast, the heavy sediment loads of such small rivers, the confluence in small areas of many of these rivers and the added problems caused by the major changes to drainage associated with breaching of the Durlston–Needles ridge. As discussed above, it is only recently that early BGS divisions, primarily on altitudinal grounds, into major groups such as "Plateau" and "Terrace" gravels have been superseded by more detailed differentiation, and there remains uncertainty over the interpretation, dating and correlation of many of the mapped units. Nonetheless there is no doubt that they generally cover the Quaternary, and it is hoped that the currently increasing

3

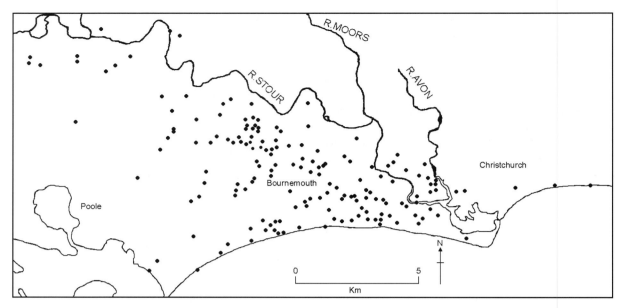

Figure 1.3: Palaeolithic find-spots around Bournemouth (after Wymer 1999: Map 23)

focus on the Solent region may lead to advances in these areas, as addressed in this volume by Bridgland (Chapter 3) and Bates (Chapter 4).

PREVIOUS RESEARCH

Following Evans' call to arms for a search of English Drift deposits for Palaeolithic implements early in the second half of the 19th century (Evans 1860: 307), the deposits of the Solent region were quickly recognised as amongst the richest. By the time of Evans' (1872) review, numerous find-spots for handaxes had been identified in Southampton and Salisbury, and in Avon Valley gravels further downstream at Downton and Ashford. "Considerable numbers" (*ibid.* 546) of handaxes — at least 60 — had also been recovered from the eastern shore of Southampton Water at Hillhead, and a single handaxe had also been found from the gravel capping the cliff-top at Barton-on-Sea. By the end of the 19th century this early promise had been more than fulfilled. Evans (1897) emphasised, for instance, the "extensive collections" from Southampton (*ibid.* 624), the "considerable number" from Hillhead (*ibid.* 625) and the "astonishing number" from Barton-on-Sea (*ibid.* 637). In the most recent survey, Wymer (1999: 105) identifies the Solent region as containing more Palaeolithic sites than anywhere else in Britain, 169 of them in Bournemouth alone (Figure 1.3). In total, over 15,000 artefacts retaining sufficient provenance to be related to sites in the Solent region are known to exist in museums across the country, over 8,500 of them handaxes (Hosfield 1999: 23, Table 2.1).

Despite the wealth of material recovered up to *c.* the 1950s, and the proven richness of the Pleistocene deposits across the Solent region, the contribution of the Solent region to subsequent Palaeolithic research is very much the dog that didn't bark in the night. Doughty (1978) notes, for instance, that hardly any palaeoliths have been recovered in Southampton since the 1920s, and despite occasional chance finds and monitoring exercises, such as at the prolific Dunbridge site (Harding 1998) — a can of worms best left unopened here, but see Chippindale (1989) — the number of major recent investigations into the Palaeolithic of the Solent region can be counted on the fingers of one leg, with the possible exception of ApSimon and Gamble's 1975 excavation at Red Barns, Portchester, right on the eastern margin of the region (Wenban-Smith *et al.* 2000), and the work of Draper (1951), and more recently, Hack (1999 & 2000) at Rainbow Bar off Hillhead, some of the material from which was displayed at this meeting. Why this curious situation has arisen is a matter for Holmes. What is important is to redress the balance, and hopefully this volume, and the day meeting from which it originated, will constitute a step in the right direction.

ARRANGEMENT OF PAPERS

The papers in the volume represent a full record of those presented at the meeting, and are reproduced here in the same order as given. The first three papers are predominantly concerned with the Pleistocene sequence and its dating. Dix provides a general introduction to the Pleistocene geology of the Solent region, looking in more detail than above at the onshore and offshore deposits of the region, their relationship with changing climate and fluctuating sea level, and introducing the possible complications of tectonic movements. Bridgland explores the potential of the Palaeolithic archaeological record to provide chronological indicators for the geological deposits, and Bates looks to the overlap with the comparatively well-dated Sussex raised beach staircase for a route into dating the Solent deposits.

The next five papers are more overtly concerned with the interpretation of Palaeolithic archaeological evidence. Roe provides a general introduction to the range of Palaeolithic sites in the region, drawing attention to some observations made by him in the 1960s, not thought by him especially interesting at the time, but the significance of which seems to have increased in the light of subsequent developments in the subject. Wenban-Smith looks at a sample of material from one specific terrace in Southampton, with a view to investigating the constancy or otherwise of the technology and typology, and considering the wider potential implications of such observations. Loader reviews the current state of knowledge of the site at Priory Bay, on the Isle of Wight, and highlights the extraordinary quantity of material recovered from the beach over years, the threat to the site posed by cliff-collapse and the lack of knowledge of the nature and Palaeolithic archaeological significance of the imminently threatened deposits. Roaming beyond the strict bounds of the Solent River region, but remaining in the unsung southwest, Marshall examines the handaxe collection from Broom, in the Axe Valley on the Dorset–Devon border, with a particular eye on the use of Greensand Chert as a raw material and the effects of raw material quality and nodule size on artefact form. In contrast to these more site-specific studies, Hosfield reconsiders the potential of disturbed archaeological material to contribute to behavioural interpretation by developing improved modelling of the taphonomic history of such material, using as examples the sites of Wood Green and Dunbridge. He concludes that the loose spatial and chronological integrity of transported material from terraces in fact makes it particularly suitable for the investigation of changing landscape exploitation and hominid demography in relation to the climatic changes of the Pleistocene.

The final paper of the day, from Wilkinson, moved the focus to the curation of the Palaeolithic archaeological heritage, and the problem of predicting the most likely locations of undisturbed sites in advance of development. The solution proposed is to construct a regional three-dimensional model of the fine-grained sediments with which one might expect such sites to be associated, to be used as the basis for identifying areas of potential significance worthy of investigation in advance of any development projects.

Overall, the collection of papers represents a snapshot of current investigations into the Palaeolithic archaeology and Pleistocene geology of the Solent River region. The diversity and complementary nature of this work, supplemented by the increasingly active concern with the curation of the resource, bodes well that the next 50 years of Palaeolithic research may put the Solent Basin more firmly on the Palaeolithic map, alongside classic areas such as the Thames Valley, East Anglia and the Sussex raised beaches.

REFERENCES

Allen, L.G. & Gibbard, P.L. 1993. Pleistocene evolution of the Solent River of southern England. *Quaternary Science Reviews* 12: 503–528.

ApSimon, A.M., Gamble, C.S. & Shackley, M.L. 1977. Pleistocene raised beaches on Ports Down, Hampshire. *Proceedings of the Hampshire Field Club and Archaeological Society* 33: 17–32.

Bates, M.R., Parfitt, S.A. & Roberts, M.B. 1997. The chronology, palaeogeography and archaeological significance of the marine Quaternary record of the West Sussex coastal plain, southern England, UK. *Quaternary Science Reviews* 16: 1227–1252.

Bridgland, D.R. 1999. Analysis of the raised beach gravel deposits at Boxgrove and related sites. In M.B. Roberts & S.A. Parfitt (ed's) *Boxgrove: a Middle Pleistocene Hominid site at Eartham Quarry, Boxgrove, West Sussex*: 100–111. English Heritage, London.

Bristow, C.R., Freshney, E.C. & Penn, I.E. 1991. *Geology of the Country around Bournemouth*. Memoir of the British Geological Survey, Sheet 329. HMSO, London.

Chippindale, C. 1989. Editorial. *Antiquity* 63: 413–416.

Department of the Environment. 1990. *Planning Policy Guidance: Archaeology and Planning*. PPG 16. HMSO, London.

Draper, J.C. 1951. Stone industries from Rainbow Bar, Hants. *Archaeological Newsletter* 3(9): 147–149.

Doughty, R.M. 1978. *An Analysis of the Spatial and Temporal Distribution of Palaeoliths from Southampton*. Unpublished BA dissertation, Department of Archaeology, University of Southampton.

Dyer, K.R. 1975. The buried channels of the "Solent River", southern England. *Proceedings of the Geologists Association* 86: 239–245.

Edwards, R.A. & Freshney, E.C. 1987. *The Geology of the Country around Southampton*. Memoir of the British Geological Survey, Sheet 315. HMSO, London.

Edwards, R.A., Scrivener, R.C. & Forster, A. 1987. *Applied geological mapping: Southampton area*. Research Report of the British Geological Survey, No. ICSO/87/2, Vol. 1. British Geological Survey, Exeter.

Evans, J. 1860. On the occurrence of flint implements in undisturbed beds of gravel, sand and clay. *Archaeologia* 38: 280–307.

Evans, J. 1872. *The Ancient Stone Implements, Weapons, and Ornaments, of Great Britain*. Longmans, Green, Reader and Dyer, London.

Evans, J. 1897, 2nd edition. *The Ancient Stone Implements, Weapons and Ornaments of Great Britain*. Longmans, London.

Fox, D.W. 1862. When and how was the Isle of Wight severed from the mainland? *The Geologist* 5: 452–454.

Hack, B. 1999. More stone tools from Rainbow Bar. *Proceedings of the Hampshire Field Club and Archaeological Society* 54: 161–171.

Hack, B. 2000. Rainbow Bar: some observations and thoughts. *Lithics* 21: 36–44.

Harding, P.A. 1998. An interim report of an archaeological watching brief on Palaeolithic deposits at Dunbridge, Hants. In N.M. Ashton, F. Healy & P.B. Pettitt (ed's) *Stone Age Archaeology: Essays in Honour of John Wymer*: 72–76. Oxbow, Oxford.

Hosfield, R.T. 1999. *The Palaeolithic of the Hampshire Basin*. BAR British Series 286. Hadrian Books, Oxford.

Preece, R.C., Scourse, J.D., Houghton, S.D., Knudsen, K.L. & Penney, D.N. 1990. The Pleistocene sea-level and neotectonic history of the eastern Solent, southern England. *Philosophical Transactions of the Royal Society of London Series B 328*: 425–477.

Roe, D.A. 1981. *The Lower and Middle Palaeolithic Periods in Britain*. Routledge & Kegan Paul, London.

Wenban-Smith, F.F. 1995. Square pegs in round holes: problems of managing the Palaeolithic heritage. In M.A. Cooper, A. Firth, J. Carman & D. Wheatley (ed's) *Managing Archaeology*: 146–162. Routledge, London.

Wenban-Smith, F.F., Gamble, C.S. & ApSimon, A.M. 2000. The Lower Palaeolithic site at Red Barns, Portchester, Hampshire: bifacial technology, raw material quality and the organisation of Archaic behaviour. *Proceedings of the Prehistoric Society* 66: 209–255.

Wymer, J.J. 1999. *The Palaeolithic Occupation of Britain*. Wessex Archaeology, Salisbury.

2. THE GEOLOGY OF THE SOLENT RIVER SYSTEM

J.K. Dix

ABSTRACT

The geology of the Hampshire Basin is dominated by Cretaceous Chalk and the, unconformably, overlying muds, sands and gravels of the early Tertiary deposits. Relatively gentle deformation of these sequences has resulted in the creation of the natural basin identified today and within which is contained the catchment of the Solent River system. This river system developed throughout the Pleistocene and as such is believed to have dominated the landscape for this entire period. There has been significant modification of the river system by every interglacial highstand, most recently with the Holocene transgression which has flooded the lower reaches of the Devensian version and as such has caused considerable re-working of the currently submerged deposits. Associated with this river system is a sporadic but well documented assemblage of Lower and Middle Palaeolithic artefacts. The existence and distribution of these assemblages is intimately linked to the underlying geology and the basin's more recent history. A synthesis of the Caenozoic and Pleistocene history is therefore presented as a backdrop to more detailed discussions presented within the rest of this volume. A short discussion of the key future research issues related to our understanding of the Solent River system will be presented.

INTRODUCTION

As will be demonstrated in many of the papers within this volume, the geology and geological history of the Solent River system has a fundamental impact on the nature and distribution of Palaeolithic material within this part of the Hampshire Basin. Firstly, there is the obvious original source of the lithic material from the Jurassic and Cretaceous sequences exposed within the catchment area. Secondly, there is a very strong association between the fluvial terrace gravel deposits associated with the course of the Solent River and identified Palaeolithic sites and findspots (Wymer 1999). Consequently, this dominance of secondary context lithic assemblages means that any interpretation of the archaeological record has to take full account of geological controls on artefact deposition (Hosfield this volume). Further, the majority of work to date has focused on currently exposed terrestrial sites (typically exploiting 19th century gravel quarries: Wilkinson this volume), however, there is growing recognition of the archaeological potential of the offshore gravel resource. This offshore material has undergone even more extensive post-depositional re-working, principally in relation to the Holocene marine transgression, and so will require a much greater understanding of current sedimentation processes than is required for the relatively benign terrestrial environments. It is also important to note that due to variable patterns of submergence, deposition and erosion related to this event that the true nature of the course of the Solent 'River/s' has only recently been investigated (Bridgland 1996; Velegrakis *et al.* 1999). Therefore this paper does not present new material but aims to present a short review of the geology of the southern part of the Hampshire Basin, with emphasis on the catchment area of the Solent River system. Comment will also be made on the submergence of the lower reaches of the catchment area during the most recent Holocene transgression, and the potential of the offshore zone for further elucidating our understanding of the Palaeolithic of the Solent region.

PRE-PLEISTOCENE GEOLOGY

The Solent and surrounding estuaries and inlets are the latest of a series of shallow-water bodies that have incised into the Mesozoic and early Tertiary rocks of the Hampshire Basin. This basin in conjunction with the London Basin to the north, the two being separated by the Chalk of the Hampshire Downs and the anticlinorium of the Weald, formed part of a single basin of deposition, the Anglo–Paris–Belgian Basin (Melville & Freshney 1982). Throughout the Mesozoic and into the early Tertiary the Hampshire Basin was in fact a series of individually subsiding basins into which seas transgressed and regressed in response to eustatic fluctuations and localised differential subsidence. The Solent River system is located in one of these sub-basins toward the southern margin of the Hampshire Basin. The area is an asymmetric elongated basin with a gently, southerly, dipping northern margin and a steeply, northerly, dipping southern margin. The southern margin is described by the Purbeck–Wight monocline, which most dramatically crops out at the Needles on the western tip of the Isle of Wight and at Handfast Point on the east coast of Dorset (Figure 2.1).

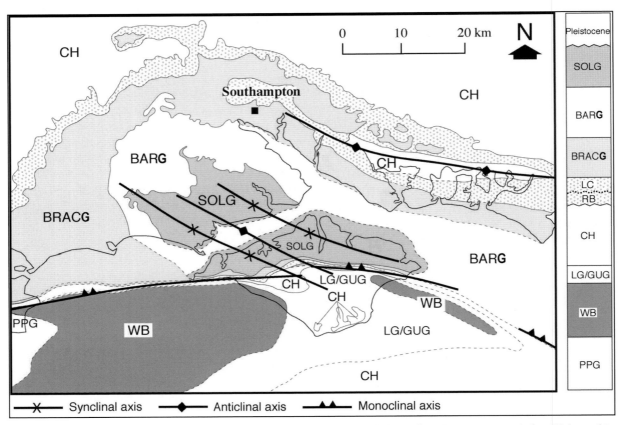

Figure 2.1: The solid geology of the middle and lower reaches of the Solent River system (after Velegrakis 2000); PPG: Portland/Purbeck Group; WB: Wealden Beds; LG/GUG: Lower Greensand/Gault and Upper Greensand; CH: Chalk; RB/LC: Reading Beds and London Clay; BRACG: Bracklesham Group; BARG: Barton Group; SOLG: Solent Group

The Cretaceous in this area is dominated by the Chalk that can be further subdivided into the Lower, Middle and Upper Chalk (Melville & Freshney 1982). Of these three sub-divisions it is the Campanian Upper Chalk that dominates, cropping out both along the southern margin (along the Purbeck–Wight monocline), the Portsdown anticline (at the head of Portsmouth, Langstone and Chichester inlets) and the high ground of the northern boundary. Flint bands within this Upper Chalk sequence are interpreted as being the source of the Pleistocene terrace gravels described below (Velegrakis 2000). Upper Jurassic and Early and Middle Cretaceous bedrock is restricted to the margins of this sub-basin. Jurassic sequences (e.g. the Portland/Purbeck group) are of minor influence only acting as a source zone of Chert in the catchment of the Frome (Bridgland this volume). These marginal localities are generally represented by outcrops of the Wealden beds (freshwater marls and estuarine/shallow marine shales) and the Lower and Upper Greensand (shallow marine sands and clays — and the principal source of Chert in the area). These sequences form the basement of the upper reaches of tributaries of the Rivers Stour, Frome and Avon as well as the now submerged lower reaches of the River Frome. The end of the Cretaceous is marked by a final regressive phase followed by a period of gentle folding and significant erosion resulting in the creation of an unconformable contact with the overlying Tertiary sequences (Figure 2.1).

A marine influence on the depositional environment continued within the Hampshire Basin throughout the Tertiary and it is sediments deposited during this period that dominate the bedrock stratigraphy in the Solent River catchment area. Again a series of marine transgressions and regressions during the Tertiary resulted in freshwater, lacustrine and brackish conditions being present in the sedimentary record. This cyclicity has produced many environments including: shallow marine shelf to beaches, tidal flats, coastal marshes, lagoons, estuaries, rivers and lakes. Muds and sandy muds dominate much of the sedimentary succession although locally sands can be important.

The basal unit of the Tertiary sequence in this area are the Palaeocene Reading Beds. The basement of the Reading Beds is a layer of large unworn flints with black/dark green exteriors, embedded in loamy glauconitic sand, resting unconformably on an eroded Upper Chalk surface. Above this basement bed the strata are dominated by red-mottled plastic clays (West 1980). Overlying the Reading Beds, with a sharp erosive junction, are sediments of the Palaeocene–Lower Eocene London Clay unit. This unit consists of silty and sandy clays, clayey silts and sandy silts which exhibit five individual coarsening upward sequences (Freshney *et al.* 1985).

The London Clay is conformably overlain by the Bracklesham Group, which includes the sands, clayey sands and sandy clays of the Bagshot Beds and Bracklesham Beds (both Eocene in age). These units in turn pass conformably into the Barton Group, which is simply subdivided into the fine grained blue-grey clays of the Barton Clays and the coarser sands, sandy clays and thinly bedded limestones of the Barton Sands. Finally the Solent Group comprises the two predominantly clastic formations of the Headon Hill Formation, the Bembridge Formation (specifically the Bembridge Limestone) and the Bouldnor Formation (Insole *et al.* 1998). The sands and sandy clays at the base of the Headon Hill Formation fine upwards through the sequence, being dominated by clays and marls with occasional limestone bands, towards its boundary with the overlying Bembridge Limestone. The Bembridge Limestone is a prominent limestone band (5–8.5m thick) which represents an easily identifiable boundary as the sediments return to clay and marl dominated sequences in the overlying Bouldnor Formation. These argillaceous sediments of the Solent Group dominate the central part of this basin and inevitably the development of the middle reaches of the Solent River system. The ease with which they are eroded can be seen in the dramatic cliff failures seen along the northwest coast of the Isle of Wight today.

The Eocene–Oligocene boundary lies somewhere within the Bouldnor Formation but its exact location is still the subject of significant debate (Insole *et al.* 1998). These lower Oligocene units of the Solent Group, whatever their thickness, represent the youngest Tertiary deposits in the area. This is a result of either non-deposition or significant erosion post the Alpine (Miocene) orogeny, the next deposits to be recorded are of Quaternary age.

Structural Geology

As described above the main Hampshire Basin is divided into a number of concealed subsidiary grabens separated by stable horsts (Melville & Freshney 1982). These features probably developed during the Mesozoic tectonically fracturing an earlier pre-Mesozoic stratigraphy that had already been deformed by the late-Palaeozoic Variscan orogeny. The geology of the areas can be defined by two distinct structural trends: one east to west and one northwest to southeast. The east–west trend is represented at depth by the fault bounded horst and graben structures, however on the surface these faults are represented by a series of asymmetric anticlines and monoclines (e.g. the dominant Isle of Wight Monocline). The absence of serious fracturing within the Cretaceous and Tertiary strata (Nowell 1995) suggest that they represent the draping of plastic Mesozoic and Tertiary strata over active basement faults. The northwest to southeast structural trend truncates and laterally displaces the east–west features and are again believed to have their origins with the early Variscan and Mesozoic tectonic events. During the Tertiary (and in particular related to the Alpine Orogeny) the majority of these ancient features were re-activated, resulting in the general bowl shaped warp of the Hampshire Basin, other more gentle east–west warps and the draped style of sedimentation indicative of the Tertiary sediments in this area. As will be demonstrated in the next section these structural components have had significant control on the development of the subsequent Solent River system.

For a more detailed review of the geology of the Hampshire Basin the reader is referred to Melville & Freshney (1982) and Hamblin *et al.* (1992) and Insole *et al.* (1998).

PLEISTOCENE GEOLOGY

The Pleistocene geology of the Hampshire Basin is dominated by the sequential development of the west to east flowing Solent River system. The hypothesis of the 'Solent River' dates back to Fox (1862), however, the pioneering work on this feature was by Reid at the turn of the 20th century. Reid (1902) recognised that a series of widespread gravel deposits found throughout Hampshire represented successive phases of fluvial deposition. These and subsequent workers hypothesised various forms of a major eastward flowing river system from the headwaters of the Rivers Frome and Piddle in the east to a major south-easterly flowing river system in the East Solent, with numerous tributaries in between (see Bridgland this volume: Figures 3.1 and 3.6). As can be seen from these figures the 'Solent River' can be traced into the Northern Palaeovalley complex which in turn is connected to the even larger Channel river system (Kellaway *et al.* 1975; Gibbard 1988, 1995).

Much of the early research was driven by the desire to establish if and when the Isle of Wight was separated from the mainland (see Tomalin 2000 for a historical review). The most comprehensive analysis of the terrestrial evidence for the 'Solent River' was undertaken by Allen (1991; Allen & Gibbard 1993). Detailed analysis of these fluvial gravel deposits suggest they are composed almost exclusively of flints with minor (cumulatively < 15%) quantities of quartz, quartzite, chert and other exotics. They rarely exceed 5–6m in thickness and are generally undisturbed by faulting or folding (West 1980). The deposits lie on a series of well-developed north-bank terraces, which descend from *c.* +123m O.D. in the northern part of the basin to -20m O.D. at the mouth of Southampton Water.

Many of the early interpretations of the Solent River inferred a major river channel crossing Poole and Christchurch Bay, then entering the West Solent and finally exiting the area via the East Solent. These interpretations relied on: geological extrapolation, with the flow of the westerly suite of rivers due south believed to have been prevented by a now submerged chalk ridge following the Purbeck–Wight Monocline (Englefield 1816); borehole/excavation data (e.g. Godwin 1940; Oakley 1943); and latterly the offshore extrapolation of thalweg gradients from terrestrial terraces (e.g. Bridgland 1996). The proliferation over the last thirty years of seismic surveys in the Poole–Christchurch–Solent region has significantly enhanced our understanding of the general morphology of the 'Solent River'. The earliest surveys focused on the East Solent (Dyer 1975) which demonstrated the submerged base of a river to reach a maximum incised depth of -46m O.D. at the entrance to the East Solent, the incised channel exhibiting marginal terraces and a thick (10's m's) post-incision fill. This same survey, however, suggested similar channel cut and fill sequences were absent in the West Solent, bedrock surface being covered by only a thin veneer of sands and gravels. This work was followed by the large scale mapping of the river valleys to the south of the Isle of Wight (Kellaway *et al.* 1975; IGS 1977; Larsonneur *et al.* 1982). These surveys demonstrated the relationship between the Northern Palaeovalley Complex and the Channel river system; and equally importantly confirmed the presence of a submerged chalk ridge connecting the Needles to Handfast Point.

Although this work provided incontrovertible evidence of offshore channels in the most easterly part of the 'Solent River' catchment, it was the work of Velegrakis (1994; Velegrakis *et al.* 1999) who provided information on the key Poole and Christchurch sections. This work identified seven Palaeovalley Complexes (I–VII: Velegrakis *et al.* 1999) within Poole and Christchurch Bay, six of which suggested they had been formed by southward flowing river systems. Of these the three most easterly palaeovalleys cut through the Purbeck–Wight ridge, suggesting river capture by steep drainage systems on the southern flank of this feature exploiting N–S faults and zones of ridge thinning (Nowell 2000), prior to the Holocene marine transgression. The major Palaeovalley Complex I was interpreted as being the offshore extension of the Frome, supporting the assertion of Bridgland (1996) based on extrapolation of thalweg gradients offshore. Of the other six complexes two (IV and V) occurred as steep drainage ducts on the southern flank of the offshore ridge and two (VI and VII) were considered too small and with elevations of their thalwegs lower than the predicted values from the terrestrial record. Palaeovalley complexes II and III were considered not to have onshore correlatives (Velegrakis *et al.* 1999) whilst their wider and less well incised form suggested that they drained only from the western half of Poole Bay (Nowell 2000).

The negative evidence of this work was also important as it suggested that there was no bedrock expression of an east–west flowing channel related to the 'Solent River'. It also suggested that the valleys that were identified had no associated gravel terraces and indeed lacked any substantial accumulations of coarse-grained fluvial material. This contrasts markedly with buried channels further east e.g. the Arun river (Bellamy 1995) which has been shown to have several generations of well-developed terraces. Interestingly, this is the opposite relationship of the terrestrial record where the terraces of the Sussex Rivers are very poorly developed when compared to those of the Solent region (Bates this volume). The morphology and sedimentary fill of these offshore palaeovalleys has therefore been used to suggest that they are either expressions of relatively juvenile rivers (Velegrakis *et al.* 1999) which have probably only existed since the Devensian (Nowell 2000); or that polycyclic denudation by a sequence of marine transgressive/regressive phases during the Pleistocene has erased any evidence of an easterly or long-term southerly flowing drainage system.

This debate raises two important questions for the study of the 'Solent River': firstly the timing of fluvial incision and terrace aggradation and secondly the impact on the stratigraphic record of marine transgressive/regressive phases (with particular emphasis on the Flandrian transgression). The first of these issues will be dealt with here whilst the second will be discussed in the section below (Holocene Geology).

The chronology of the 'Solent River' has been the subject of serious debate since the original hypotheses for its existence were proposed. It is commonly agreed that the rivers responsible for channel incision and fluvial aggradation, were very high energy, in a pro-glacial setting and were grading to base levels several 10's if not 100's metres below current mean sea level. It has been proposed that they represent cyclic re-occupation of a drainage pattern, initiated in the Pliocene (Bridgland this volume), and developed throughout the Pleistocene. It has been suggested (Bates this volume; Bridgland this volume) that the terraces have been created in response to changing climatic fluctuations throughout this period, and in a setting of progressive and consistent uplift. A model for the development of climatic controls on terrace formation in the Solent system is presented in Bridgland (this volume). Although as discussed by Bates (this volume) the underlying assumption of invariant uplift may be suspect as the rate and pattern of uplift in the English Channel area during the Pleistocene may in fact be very complex (van Vliet-Lanoë *et al.* 2000).

The morphological and geological work undertaken to date provides a basic chronological context for river development based on Pleistocene climate cycles, but more accurate chronologies are the topic of significant recent research. Dating of the terrace sequences in particular is being attempted in three complimentary ways:

1. Dating of intercalated organic materials: dateable interglacial sediments are commonly used to provide chronologies for gravel terraces but within the Solent system such deposits are rare and indeed totally absent from the middle and upper terrace sequences. Only the two lowest sequences, the Lepe and Pennington Gravels have dateable material in context. These give dates of OIS 7 (Allen *et al.* 1996; Bridgland & Schreve in press) and OIS 5e (Allen *et al.* 1996) respectively.

2. Comparison with the marine/coastal record: Bates (Bates *et al.* 1997; Bates this volume) presents a model for linking the fluvial deposits that dominate the Solent river region with marine deposits of the West Sussex Coastal Plain. This model enables terrace correlation with four altitudinally and temporally distinct sequences of the coastal plain east of Portsmouth: Goodwood–Slindon Raised Beach (+32–+43m O.D.: OIS 13); Aldingbourne Raised Beach (+17.5–+27.5m O.D.: OIS?); the Brighton–Norton Raised Beach (+5–+12m O.D.: OIS 7); and the Pagham Raised beach (-2–+3m O.D.: OIS 5e). His synthesised

chronology is presented in Bates (this volume: Table 4.2).

3. The archaeological record: Bridgland (this volume) uses the distribution of Palaeolithic artefacts between the terraces and analogy with the Thames estuary sequence to ascribe ages to two of the major Middle Pleistocene terraces. This technique gives dates for the Old Milton Gravel and the Taddiford Farm Gravel of OIS 11/10 and OIS 9/8 respectively. Discrepancies in the dates from 2. and 3. are still to be explored.

Finally dating of the offshore record is even more circumspect with no chronology existing at present. Attempts to date offshore events have either been by extrapolation of the still incomplete terrestrial chronology offshore or by qualitative interpretation of channel form and fill deposits. The problems encountered can be illustrated by the dating of the southerly extension of the Frome into Poole Bay. Bridgland (1996) on the basis of onshore–offshore correlation predicted that the Frome drained to the south and suggested on the basis of terrace gradients and the Palaeolithic record that this must have occurred by the Middle Pleistocene. Indeed he also suggested that only the highest surviving gravels in the Frome catchment could have represented part of a major eastwardly flowing 'Solent River'. By contrast Velegrakis *et al.* (1999) confirmed the presence of a southerly flowing channel associated with the Frome but as described earlier suggested that they were the product of a very young (Devensian or later) river system. Velegrakis *et al.* (1999) attempted to support this date by correlating the offshore thalweg gradients to the onshore terrace deposits, identifying the East Holme Gravel and the Stoborough Gravels as the most likely correlatives. A similar exercise was undertaken by Allen & Gibbard (1993) on the basis of correlation of the East Holme Gravel with a single altitude point for a channel (no orientation given) identified in Christchurch Bay by Dyer (1975). Ironically Allen & Gibbard suggest that as this channel represents the westerly extension of the Devensian (Dyer 1975) buried channel of the East Solent the correlated onshore gravel terraces are of an equivalent age. Unfortunately, Dyer (1975) uses a chronology based simply on a single cycle of marine regression during the Pleistocene, which terminates with a lowstand in the Devensian, thus allowing the Solent rivers to develop uninterrupted.

Consequently, despite the fact that recent geophysical surveys have provided a detailed map of the incised bedrock surface, the distribution and nature of channel fill deposits and the nature of the current seabed sediments there is still no definitive resolution of either the palaeo-drainage patterns of the Solent River system/s or their chronology. We are therefore still left with two conflicting theories for both problems. Firstly, the absence of any east–west flowing drainage channels in Poole Bay, Christchurch Bay and for that matter the West Solent is representative of either a segmented drainage pattern with a dominantly southerly flow or extensive poly-cyclic erosion during the transgressive-regressive phases of the Pleistocene. Velegrakis *et al.* (1999) favour the latter explanation whilst Tomalin (2000) prefers the former. Indeed Tomalin (2000) uses the absence of major easterly flowing channels to invoke Reid's (1905) concept of a central West Solent Isthmus separating the river systems of Poole and Christchurch Bay from those of Southampton Water and the East Solent. At present neither theory can be supported with confidence, the issue will hopefully be resolved by future intensive study of the critical West Solent sections.

Secondly, the issue of dating the offshore sequences will always be problematic, particularly considering the ongoing discussions on the chronology of the onshore terraces presented in Bridgland (this volume) and Bates (this volume). In the case of Poole and Christchurch Bay this results in a major incision phase occurring either in the Middle Pleistocene (Bridgland 1996) or the Late Devensian (Velegrakis *et al.* 1999). In the absence of any directly recovered core material from the offshore terraces and river channels the chronology is always going to rely on extrapolation of thalweg gradients. However, considering the problems of qualitative and quantitative interpretation of seismic sections ("...the offshore [bedrock] bathymetry obtained by Velegrakis (1994) is markedly dissimilar in places to that obtained by the BGS (1990)...": Nowell 2000: 505) this has to be regarded as being a dangerous route toward defining a chronology.

HOLOCENE GEOLOGY

The final stage in the geological history of this region is one of a marine transgression post-dating the Devensian maximum. This transgression is the product of both eustatic (global) components, related to the melting of these Devensian maximum ice sheets, and isostatic (local) components, the product of crustal flexure typically in response to the retreat of such ice masses. Superimposed on these changes are variations in palaeotidal ranges (controlled by the volume of the tidal prism e.g. Shennan *et al.* 1999), magnitude and frequency of storm events and local patterns of sedimentation and erosion. These can produce variations in the rate of sea level change on decadal scales and patterns of coastal change on 100's metres to kilometre scales. The combined effects of these processes are frequently represented by local or regional sea-level curves which have been constructed from a combination of stratigraphic, geomorphic and archaeological data (e.g. Long & Roberts 1997).

Little is known of the immediate post-glacial period but for the southern UK, Devensian glacial maximum sea levels (*c.* 18,000 BP: OIS 2–3) were believed to have been at *c.* -130m O.D. with the subsequent rapid sea-level rise being dominated by post-glacial eustatic changes. By *c.* 10,000 years BP in the English Channel sea level was still below -30m O.D. (Long & Scaife pers. comm.). This would place the Solent coastline to the south of the Isle of Wight, although even at this early stage tidal influence may have penetrated someway inland along the course of the Solent River. Variations in the sea level record change across the Solent River catchment area, but Long & Scaife (forthcoming) have produced an integrated relative sea level curve for the Solent region. This work suggests that sharply increasing sea levels continued throughout the early Holocene reaching an altitude of *c.* -15m O.D. at *c.* 8,500 cal. years BP. By the start of the middle Holocene at *c.* 8,000 cal. years BP relative sea levels had risen to *c.* -15m O.D., but rate of rise starts to decrease achieving *c.* -6m O.D. by 6,000 cal. years BP. This rate of change slows even further over the next 3,500 years with RSL rising to *c.* -2m O.D. by *c.* 2,500 cal years BP. As with many areas along the south coast few data points exist for the last 2,000 years although it is assumed that sea level did not exceed 0m O.D. during this period.

Bring together the regional sea level data with the seismo-stratigraphic data of Velegrakis *et al.* (1999) can provide a hypothesis for the inundation of the Solent River system from the west (to date similar attempts have not been made for the Eastern Solent). The channel fill stratigraphies of the Palaeovalley Complexes vary across the Bays. The western Palaeovalley Complexes of Poole Bay have a fill stratigraphy indicative of a transition from fluvial to fluvial-estuarine to marine conditions. This is typical of a Type-I incised valley depositional sequence (Posamentier & Vail 1988) which consists of sediments associated with Lowstand (LST), transgressive (TST) and Highstand (HST) system tracts. By contrast transgressive system tracts (TST) dominate the easterly Palaeovalley Complexes of Christchurch Bay. This suggests that inundation of the two areas was markedly different with Poole Bay being inundated first and in a relatively constant, uniform, manner with the sea entering via the river channels and then flooding the interfluves. The formation of Christchurch Bay probably followed, but in a more abrupt manner, possibly via catastrophic breaching of the eastern section of the Wight–Purbeck ridge and Christchurch Ledges. The high energy environment suggested by such a transition may be partly responsible for the high levels of erosion and sediment redistribution supposedly responsible for the removal of an earlier and more developed 'Solent River' system. The absence of any terraces or significant fluvial material and the presence of large gravel banks (e.g. the Shingles and Dolphin Banks) suggest significant recent reworking of material. The final phase of this transition was the flooding of the Western Solent and the separation of the Isle of Wight from the mainland. Palaeoenvironmental evidence on which the Solent regional sea level curve was based (Long & Scaife forthcoming) would suggest that this process had started by *c.* 8,500 years BP.

It is interesting to note that the very different sedimentary sequences of Poole and Christchurch Bay and for that matter between the West and East Solent (the latter having a thick, stratified sequence of post-incisional sediments) occur under the same general very rapid rise in sea-level particularly between *c.* 12,000 cal BP and *c.* 8,000 cal BP. Similarly, palaeovalleys of other sections of the Northern Palaeovalley complex (e.g. Arun: Bellamy 1995) are typified by lowstand system tract (LST) sequences. This would suggest that either regional/local response of coastal systems to sea level rise is very variable or that the preserved sequences are more indicative of pre-transgressive variations in river architecture.

CONCLUSIONS

This paper has hopefully provided the reader with a brief resume of the geology of the Solent River system. Hopefully, the geological controls on both the form of the Solent River system as well as the Palaeolithic materials it contains is now evident. However, despite 150 years of research many questions remained unanswered. Firstly, despite recent attempts to interrogate the offshore record it is still not clear if there ever was a single 'Solent River' or if the region was cut by a series of north–south trending rivers in the west and a substantially smaller eastward flowing river system with its headwaters associated with the Western Solent and adjacent tributaries. This work has also highlighted the variability in the nature of the Pleistocene fluvial architecture across the area. This is particularly well illustrated by the dramatic decrease in the number of terrestrial terraces as you move west to east across the region compared to the inverse relationship for the submerged terrace record. Whether this relationship is in response to fluvial processes or variable preservation during transgressive phases is still unclear. Similarly, the dating of the river system (both onshore and offshore) requires much further work. Our knowledge of the terrestrial chronology is improving all the time (see Bridgland this volume; Bates this volume) but our understanding of the offshore sequences and even their relationship if any to onshore successions is still woefully poor. Finally, much thought has now been directed toward the potential of the offshore to provide new Palaeolithic sites. Consequently, the development of a more accurate and chronologically controlled series of palaeogeographic maps has to be seen as a priority, as they could provide crucial data for the creation of predictive migration models. However, despite the work of Hosfield (this volume) on the importance of secondary contexts to our understanding of the Palaeolithic, it is not clear if a useful record could survive the dynamics of successive marine transgressive and regressive cycles. Indeed it may be prudent to focus investigations in the offshore on marginal, low energy, and hence high preservation potential localities, as has been successfully achieved for a submerged Mesolithic site off Bouldnor Cliff in the West Solent (Momber 2000).

ACKNOWLEDGEMENTS

This work really only requires the thanks to the editors Francis Wenban-Smith and Rob Hosfield for patience above and beyond the call of duty.

REFERENCES

Allen, L.G. 1991. The evolution of the Solent River system during the Pleistocene. Unpublished Ph.D. thesis, University of Cambridge.

Allen, L.G. & Gibbard, P.L. 1993. Pleistocene evolution of the Solent River of southern England. *Quaternary Science Reviews* 12: 503–528.

Allen, L.G., Gibbard, P.L., Pettitt, M.E., Preece, R.C. & Robinson, J.E. 1996. Late Pleistocene deposits at Pennington Marshes, Lymington, Hampshire, Southern England. *Proceedings of the Geologists' Association* 107: 39–50.

Bates, M.R., Parfitt, S.A. & Roberts, M.B. 1997. The chronology, palaeogeography and archaeological significance of the marine Quaternary record of the West Sussex Coastal Plain, Southern England. *Quaternary Science Reviews* 16: 1227–1252.

Bellamy, A.G. 1995. Extension of the British landmass: evidence from shelf sediment bodies in the English Channel. In R.C. Preece (ed.) *Island Britain: a Quaternary perspective*: 47–62. Geological Society Special Publication No. 96. Geological Society, London.

Bridgland, D.R. 1996. Quaternary river terrace deposits as a framework for the Lower Palaeolithic record. In C.S. Gamble & A.J. Lawson (ed's) *The English Palaeolithic Reviewed*: 23–39. Wessex Archaeology, Salisbury.

Bridgland, D.R. and Schreve, D.C. (in press). River terrace formation in synchrony with long-term climatic fluctuation: examples from southern Britain. In D. Maddy, M. Macklin & J. Woodward (ed's) *River Basin Sediments Systems: Archives of Environmental Change*. Balkema, Rotterdam.

Dyer, K.R. 1975. The buried channels of the 'Solent River', southern England. *Proceedings of the Geologists' Association* 86: 239–246.

Englefield, H.C. 1816. *A Description of the principle picturesque beauties, antiquities and geological phenomena of the Isle of Wight*. London, 292 pp.

Fox, W.D. 1862. When and how was the Isle of Wight separated from the mainland? *Geologist* 5: 452.

Freshney, E.C., Bristow, C.R. & Williams, B.J. 1985.

Geology of the Sheet SZ09 (Bournemouth–Poole–Wimborne, Dorset). Geological Report of the Department of the Environment: Land Use Planning. British Geological Society, Exeter.

Gibbard, P.L. 1988 The history of the great northwest European rivers during the past three million years. *Philosophical Transactions of the Royal Society of London Series B318*, 559–602.

Gibbard, P.L. 1995. The formation of the Strait of Dover. In R.C. Preece (ed.) *Island Britain: a Quaternary perspective*: 15–26. Geological Society Special Publication No. 96. Geological Society, London.

Godwin, H., 1940. Pollen analysis and forest history of England and Wales. *New Phytologist* 39: 270–400.

Hamblin, R.J.O., Crosby, A., Balson, P.S., Jones, S.M., Chadwick, R.A., Penn, I.E. & Arthur, M.J. 1992. *The Geology of the English Channel*. British Geological Survey, United Kingdom Offshore Regional Report. HMSO, London.

Insole A., Daley B. & Carbe A. 1998. *The Isle of Wight Geological Association Guide, Number 60*: 18–23, 114–119

Institute of Geological Sciences. 1977, 1st edition. *Wight. Sheet 50°N 02°W. Solid Geology. 1:2,500,000*.

Kellaway, G.A., Redding, J.K., Shephard-Thorn, E.R. & Destombes, J.P. 1975. The Quaternary history of the English Channel. *Philosophical Transactions of the Royal Society of London Series A279*: 189–218.

Larsonneur, C., Bouysee, P. & Auffret, J-P. 1982. The superficial sediments of the English Channel and Western Approaches. *Sedimentology* 29: 851–864.

Long, A.J. & Roberts, D.H. 1997. Sea-level Change. In M. Fulford, T.C. Champion & A.J. Long (ed's). *England's Coastal Heritage: a Survey for English Heritage and the RCHME*: 25–49. English Heritage Archaeological Report 15. English Heritage, London.

Melville, R.V. and Freshney, E.C. 1982. *The Hampshire Basin and adjoining areas*. 4th edition. British Regional Geology Series. HMSO, London.

Momber, G. 2000. Drowned and deserted. A submerged prehistoric landscape in the Solent, England. *International Journal of Nautical Archaeology* 29.1: 86–99.

Nowell, D.A.G. 1995. Faults in the Purbeck–Isle of Wight Monocline. *Proceedings of the Geologists' Association*, 106: 145–150.

Nowell, D.A.G. 2000. Discussion on late Quaternary evolution of the upper reaches of the Solent River, Southern England, based upon marine geophysical evidence. *Journal of the Geological Society of London* 157: 505–507.

Oakley, K.P. 1943. A note on the post-glacial submergence of the Solent margin. *Proceeding of the Prehistoric Society* 9: 56–59.

Posamentier, H.W. & Vail, P.R. 1988. Eustatic controls on clastic deposition II-sequences and system tract models. In C.K. Wilgus, B.S. Hastings, C.G. Kendall, H.W. Posamentier, C.A. Ross & J.C. van Wagoner (ed's) *Sea level change — an integrated approach*: 125–154. Society of Economic Palaeontologists and Mineralogists Special Publications 42.

Reid, C. 1902. The geology of the country around Ringwood. *Memoir of the British Geological Survey, Sheet 314*. HMSO, London.

Reid, C. 1905. The Island of Ictis. *Archaeologia* 59: 218–288.

Shennan, I., Lambeck, K., Flather, R., Wingfield, R. Horton, B.P., McArthur, J.J., Innes, J.B., Lloyd, J.L. & Rutherford, M.M. 1999. Modelling western North Sea palaeogeographies and tidal changes during the Holocene. In I. Shennan & J.E. Andrews (ed's) *Holocene land-ocean interaction and environmental change around the western North Sea*. Geological Society Special Publication. Geological Society, London.

Tomalin, D. 2000. Geomorphological evolution of the Solent Seaway and the severance of Wight: a Review. In M.B. Collins & K. Ansell (ed's) *Solent Science — A Review*: 9–19. Proceedings in Marine Science Series. Elsevier, Amsterdam.

van Vliet-Lanoë, B., Laurent, M., Bahain, J.L., Balescu, S., Falguères, C., Field, M., Hallégouët, S. & Keen, D.H. 2000. Middle Pleistocene raised beach anomalies in the English Channel: regional and global stratigraphic implications. *Journal of Geodynamics* 29: 15–41.

Velegrakis, A.F. 1994. *Aspects of morphology and sedimentology of a transgressional embayment system: Poole and Christchurch Bays, Southern England*. Unpublished Ph.D. Thesis University of Southampton

Velegrakis, A.F. 2000. Geology, geomorphology and sediments of the Solent System. In M.B. Collins & K. Ansell (ed's) *Solent Science — A Review*: 21–43. Proceedings in Marine Science Series. Elsevier, Amsterdam.

Velegrakis, A.F., Dix, J.K. & Collins, M.B. 1999. Late Quaternary evolution of the upper reaches of the Solent River, Southern England, based upon marine geophysical evidence. *Journal of the Geological Society of London* 156: 73–87.

West, I.M. 1980. Geology of the Solent estuarine system. In NERC *The Solent Estuarine System*: 6–19. NERC Publication, Series C, No. 22. NERC, Swindon.

Wymer, J.J. 1999. *The Lower Palaeolithic occupation of Britain*. Wessex Archaeology and English Heritage, Salisbury.

3. THE PLEISTOCENE EVOLUTION AND PALAEOLITHIC OCCUPATION OF THE SOLENT RIVER

D.R. Bridgland

ABSTRACT

The Solent River, its valley now beneath the seaway between the Isle of Wight and the English mainland, was an important agent of drainage in the Hampshire Basin throughout the Pleistocene. During this time it left an extensive staircase of north-bank terraces, now forming the hinterland to the south coast, with comparable terraces extending up the more important tributary rivers. Many of the terraces dating from the Middle Pleistocene contain Lower Palaeolithic artefacts, although these are absent from the older terraces, which pre-date human occupation, and from the lowest terraces and valley-floor gravels, which signifies the disappearance of humans from Britain prior to the last interglacial. Only the last two interglacials are directly represented within the sedimentological sequences of the Solent and its tributaries, so it is necessary to turn to other evidence to assess the ages of the higher terraces. Palaeolithic archaeology, perhaps surprisingly, provides a number of age indications. The first appearance of artefacts is thought likely to be around 600,000 years ago; then twisted ovates are prevalent in assemblages from OIS 11, suggesting that the Old Milton Gravel incorporates material of that age; finally Levallois technique appears in the Taddiford Farm Gravel, which by analogy with the Thames is therefore thought to date from around the OIS 9/8 transition. The Solent has more Middle Pleistocene terraces than other UK rivers, perhaps because rejuvenation has taken place twice during each climatic cycle. The age indications from the archaeological data enable some attempt at modelling the formation of these terraces in response to both climate change and background uplift, although the results remain speculative.

INTRODUCTION

The strait that separates the Isle of Wight from the English mainland has its origins in one of Britain's largest river systems, since it is the drowned valley of a river that, for virtually the whole of the Pleistocene, formed the west to east axial drainage of the Hampshire Basin syncline (Figure 3.1). This river, first hypothesized by Fox (1862), became known as the River Solent or proto-Solent (e.g. Evans 1872; Reid 1902; Bristow *et al.* 1991). It was effectively obliterated, although perhaps only temporarily, by the Holocene marine transgression, but its former presence is recorded by the extensive north-bank terrace staircase that it has left (Allen & Gibbard 1993; Gibbard & Allen 1994; Figures 3.2–3.4). The drowned extension of the Solent River valley can be

recognized beneath the English Channel, to the east and south-east of the Isle of Wight (BGS Offshore 1:250,000 Geology Map, Wight sheet, 50°N 02°W, Sea Bed Sediments and Quaternary; Hamblin *et al.* 1992; Figure 3.5). The River Frome, which drains southern Dorset into Poole Harbour, has generally been identified as the vestigial Solent River (Everard 1954; Small 1964; West 1980; Nicholls 1987; Allen & Gibbard 1993). However Bridgland (1996) recently suggested that the pre-Holocene Frome flowed not into the Solent, but into a separate valley system that drained southwards, to the west of the Isle of Wight, into the English Channel River (cf. Nicholls 1987).

The Solent terrace system has long been recognized as a prolific source of Palaeolithic artefacts (Evans 1872, 1897; Reid 1902; Bury 1923; Wessex Archaeology 1993; Hosfield 1999), second in

15

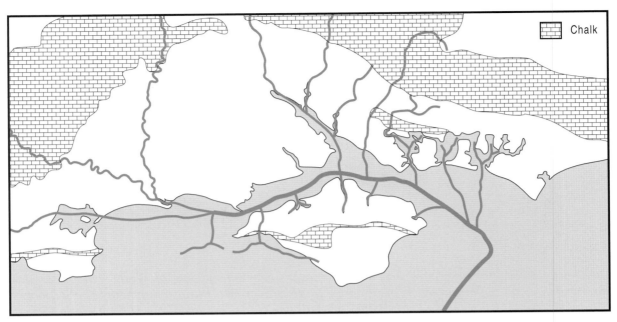

Chalk

Figure 3.1: the Solent River drainage system, as envisaged by most workers prior to the availability of offshore data; based on Everard (1954) and Allen & Gibbard (1993)

importance only to the Thames. Unlike the Thames, the Solent catchment lies entirely beyond the influence of the Pleistocene ice sheets, so that its drainage was never glacially disrupted. The Solent terrace staircase has been widely regarded as extending back to the Lower Pleistocene or even the Pliocene (Reid 1902; Allen & Gibbard 1993; Gibbard & Preece 1999). Another difference in comparison with the Thames system is that fossiliferous interglacial sediments are scarce in the Solent and are completely unknown within the middle and upper parts of the staircase (Figure 3.4). This means that there are few means of dating the terraces, Palaeolithic artefacts representing perhaps the best available evidence (Bridgland 1996).

A full reappraisal of the terrace gravels of the Solent and its tributaries in the area west of Southampton was undertaken in the late 1980s by Allen (1991; Allen & Gibbard 1993). She established a system of lithostratigraphical nomenclature for the Solent terraces and carried out detailed clast-lithological analyses of the gravels. These analyses demonstrated that the gravels are made up mainly of flint (85–98%), with small quantities of quartz, quartzite, chert and other rocks. Much of the chert comes from the Upper Greensand, outcrops of which occur in the Frome, Stour and Avon catchments. Some of it is thought, however, to have been derived from Jurassic sources that are confined to the catchment of the Frome. Of these, *Rhaxella* chert from the Portlandian of Dorset is particularly distinctive. Allen & Gibbard's Table 2 shows that these Jurassic cherts were generally more common in the older, higher-level gravels.

Allen paid little attention to the Palaeolithic

evidence from the Solent, but her revised classification was adopted by Wymer (in Wessex Archaeology 1993; Wymer 1999) when he reviewed the artefact distribution in this catchment as part of the Southern Rivers Palaeolithic Project. Bridgland (1996) was therefore able to use Wymer's newly assembled database of Solent basin find-spots in an attempt to use the artefactual content of the gravels as a means of assessing their approximate ages and correlating between the western and eastern Solent catchments.

THE PALAEOLITHIC RECORD FROM THE SOLENT

The most important concentrations of Palaeolithic find-spots in the Solent are in the Bournemouth and Southampton areas, where they largely coincide with old quarries or building sites. Although the distribution is partly controlled by the location of activities of this sort, there is also an important relationship with position in the terrace staircase. If it can be assumed that most artefacts come from the terrace deposit upon which they are found, the majority has come from the three terraces formed by the Old Milton Gravel, the Taddiford Farm Gravel and the Stanswood Bay Gravel or their equivalents in the lower reaches of tributary valleys (Figure 3.2). Of these, the Taddiford Farm Gravel would appear to be the richest source of artefacts, especially in the area of Bournemouth. The highest terrace deposit to have yielded artefacts is probably the Setley Plain Gravel (Figures 3.2 and 3.4).

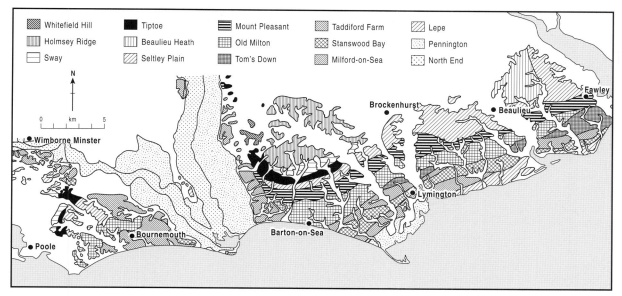

Figure 3.2: map of the terrace gravels of the Solent River between Poole and Fawley; after Allen (1991); Allen & Gibbard (1993)

Most find-spots have yielded single or small numbers of items, but there is also a concentration of rich sites in the Bournemouth area. These are generally old gravel pits, such as at Canford (SZ 026980), Corfe Mullen (SY 990980), Redhill Common (SZ 070964), King's Park, Boscombe (SZ 118929), Queen's Park, Boscombe (SZ 110934) and Pokesdown (SZ 129918). All of these are in the Taddiford Farm Gravel of the Solent River or the equivalent Ensbury Park Gravel of the Stour (Wessex Archaeology 1993; Bridgland 1996). The richest sites are at Corfe Mullen and King's Park, which have yielded handaxe numbers running into hundreds.

There is less Palaeolithic material from the Frome, with the West Knighton Gravel of Allen & Gibbard (1993) the richest source of artefacts. One locality, at Moreton (SY 780886), has produced at least 70 handaxes (Arkell 1947; Wessex Archaeology 1993). Bridgland (1996) suggested, on the basis of the patterns of archaeological richness in the areas west and east of Poole Harbour, that the West Knighton Gravel was the Frome equivalent of the Taddiford Farm Gravel of the main Solent River. However, it is clear from the long profiles reconstructed from each area by Allen & Gibbard (1993) that the West Knighton Gravel Frome could not have flowed into the Taddiford Farm Gravel Solent (Figure 3.3; see below).

The concentration of artefacts in the Taddiford Farm Gravel/Ensbury Park Gravel invites comparison with the Lynch Hill of the Thames, regarded by Wymer (1988) as the richest Palaeolithic source amongst the Thames terraces. The first appearance of artefacts in the Solent terrace staircase at the Setley Plain Gravel level suggests a date for that deposit somewhere towards the end of the Cromerian Complex, by comparison with the oldest artefact-bearing deposits in Britain for which ages have been suggested, such as at Boxgrove (Roberts 1986; Roberts *et al.* 1994), High Lodge (Ashton *et al.* 1992) and Westbury-sub-Mendip (Bishop 1982; Preece & Parfitt 2000).

Whereas the mere presence of artefacts and their relative abundance may give some indications of age, lithic technology and typology may provide more precise dating evidence. Recent suggestions that certain aspects of artefact typology have an age significance are a far cry from earlier schemes based on handaxe type, the application of which often involved inverting the expected chronological sequence of river terraces (e.g. King & Oakley 1936). The new thinking is not based on a hypothesized advancement in lithic technology, but on empirical observations of the occurrence of different types of Lower Palaeolithic artefacts in well dated sequences, such as that of the Thames, and the extrapolation of this evidence to poorly dated sequences such as the Solent.

One significant innovation that appears not to be represented in the earliest Palaeolithic assemblages in Britain, and therefore to provide an indication of age, is the Levallois technique. This appears in the Thames sequence in the youngest sediments of the Lynch Hill/Corbets Tey Terrace, at sites such as Purfleet (Essex), and is then well represented in the deposits of the succeeding Taplow/Mucking Terrace (Bridgland 1994, 1996, 1998). According to the dating scheme for the Thames terraces advocated by Bridgland (1994), this places the appearance of Levallois at the beginning of (cold) Oxygen Isotope Stage (OIS) 8, although it is clear from evidence at sites such as Crayford (Bridgland 1994, 1998; Wymer 1999), that the technique persisted into the subsequent interglacial, OIS 7. Humans then vacated Britain

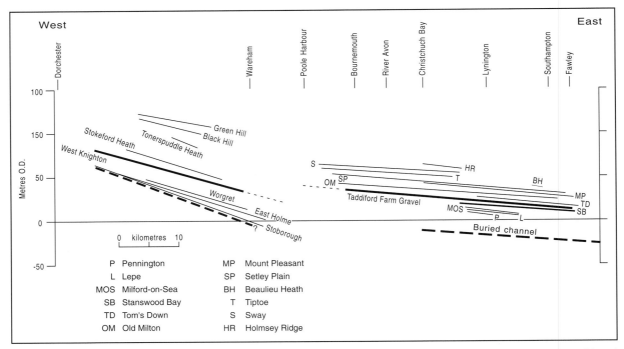

Figure 3.3: long profiles of the Solent and Frome terrace surfaces, modified from Allen & Gibbard (1993); the terraces that are the most prolific sources of artefacts, formed by the West Knighton Gravel in the west and the Taddiford Farm Gravel in the east, are highlighted

during the very cold OIS 6 glacial, which coincided with the maximum Pleistocene glaciation of the near Continent, and didn't return until the last glacial. Thus Levallois sites can be dated with some precision to OIS 8/7, although it is possible that Levallois artefacts will be eventually discovered in late OIS 9 deposits. In the Solent sequence there is a small but significant Levallois component amongst assemblages from the Taddiford Farm Gravel and its equivalents, although it is absent in higher terrace deposits. This again invites comparison with the Lynch Hill/Corbets Tey Gravel of the Thames. No Levallois artefacts are, however, recorded from the supposedly equivalent West Knighton Gravel, although there are a few Levallois cores and flakes from localities in the Frome catchment (Wessex Archaeology 1993). The appearance of Levallois technique in the Taddiford Farm Gravel of the Solent, by comparison with the better dated Thames sequence, thus suggests an age for the former deposit at around 300,000 BP, close to the OIS 9/8 transition (Bridgland 1996).

White (1998) has recently suggested that another typological variety of artefact may carry age significance, in this case ovate handaxes with twisted edges. Roe (1968) had noted that certain assemblages contained significant numbers of such implements, which are uncommon in the Britain Lower Palaeolithic as a whole. Reviewing these occurrences in the light of the better dating evidence available since 1968 led White to note that all those for which dates are available seem to belong to late in OIS 11. Important to his reasoning was the high concentration of twisted ovates in the Upper Loam at Swanscombe.

He thus suggested that twisted ovates, which do not occur in the earlier industries at sites such as Boxgrove, are, when found in abundance, a potential indicator for OIS 11.

Roe (1968) recorded a significant twisted ovate component in one assemblage from the Solent, that from Barton Cliffs. These cliffs are formed in the Old Milton Gravel of the Solent River (Figure 3.2), Although no independent dating evidence is available for the Old Milton Gravel, White's hypothesis can be tested to some degree by looking at the stratigraphical position of this formation within the Solent sequence, particularly in relation to the terraces already tentatively dated on the basis of their artefact content. It is immediately apparent that the Old Milton Gravel is in approximately the right stratigrapical position for an OIS 11 component to be anticipated, falling between the Setley Plain Gravel, in which artefacts first appear, and the Taddiford Farm Gravel, the oldest formation in which Levallois occurs. That is not to say that the Old Milton Gravel represents OIS 11 directly. It is perhaps more likely to date from the OIS 11–10 (cooling) transition, the artefacts having been swept into the river from surfaces occupied during OIS 11. White's hypothesis thus provides a tentative basis for broad correlation between the Old Milton Gravel of the Solent and the Boyn Hill/Orset Heath Formation of the Thames, which incorporates OIS 11 interglacial deposits (with twisted ovates) at Swanscombe and Dartford Heath. However, whereas in the Thames the Boyn Hill is the terrace immediately above the Lynch Hill, in the Solent there is another terrace between the Old Milton Gravel and

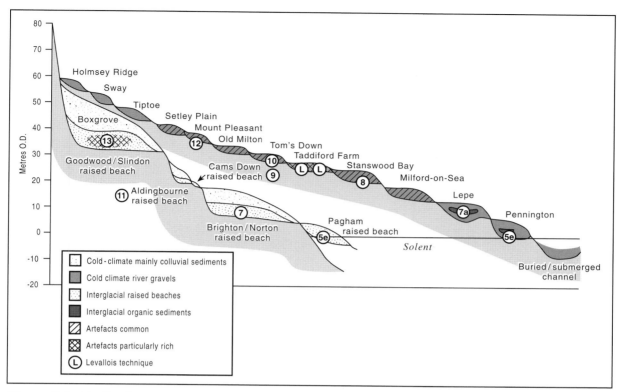

Figure 3.4: idealized transverse section through the Solent terrace staircase, projected to Christchurch with the occurrence of Palaeolithic artefacts indicated; the raised beach staircase of the Sussex coastal plain (after Bates et al. *1998) is shown for comparison*

the Taddiford Farm Gravel, likened above to the Lynch Hill of the Thames. This is because the Solent has formed more Middle Pleistocene terraces than the Thames, a problem that will be examined below.

INDEPENDENT MEANS OF DATING THE SOLENT TERRACES

As has been stated already, the Solent sequence is poorly dated, largely because it contains little in the way of interglacial fossil-bearing sediments of the sort that have provided the dating control in the Thames. Particularly important in the Thames have been mammalian remains (Schreve 1997; Bridgland & Schreve in press) and molluscan assemblages (Preece 1995, 1999), which have supplemented and enhanced the biostratigraphical control previously available from pollen (West 1969; Hollin 1977; Gibbard 1994). Calcareous ground-water is an important requirement for the long-term preservation of bones, teeth and shells, and this is lacking in most of the Solent catchment. Nevertheless the lowest two Solent terrace formations do have interglacial sediments preserved within them. The youngest of these occurs within the Pennington Gravel beneath Pennington Marshes, where it has been studied by borehole (Allen *et al.* 1996). It has been attributed to the last interglacial, the Ipswichian (=OIS 5e). Comparable sediments have also been discovered beneath the floodplain of

the Avon, at Ibsley (Barber & Brown 1987). In the next youngest terrace, formed by the Lepe Gravel (Figure 3.4), interglacial sediments again occur between lower and upper gravels, this time accessible on the modern foreshore at Stone Point (Reid 1893; West & Sparks 1960; Brown *et al.* 1975). Formerly regarded as Ipswichian (West & Sparks 1960; West 1987; Green & Keen 1987), these deposits are now attributed to OIS 7 (Allen *et al.* 1996; Bridgland & Schreve in press). The biostratigraphy at Stone Point is somewhat equivocal and the most persuasive arguments for a pre-Ipswichian age stem from terrace stratigraphy and the occurrence of an interglacial soil developed in loam above the Lepe Upper Gravel that must itself be of Last Interglacial age (Reynolds 1987).

There is no biostratigraphical evidence from any older Solent terrace, but comparison is possible with the raised beach sequence of the south coast, which includes the important fossiliferous sediments at Boxgrove, dated to the late Cromerian Complex (cf. Preece & Parfitt 2000; Bates this volume). Plotting of the Solent terrace sequence on an idealized transverse section (Figure 3.4) shows a striking correspondence between the heights of terraces in the Bournemouth area and of raised beaches on the Sussex coast. Ages attributed to the latter on the basis of biostratigraphy compare closely with ages claimed for Solent terraces at comparable heights on the basis of Palaeolithic archaeology (Figure 3.4). The raised beaches and

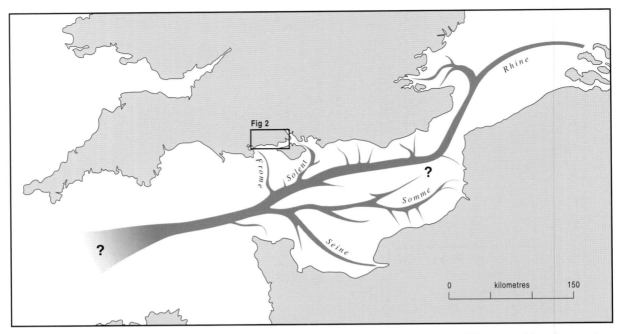

Figure 3.5: map of the last glacial English Channel River system, based on offshore rockhead mapping, modified from Lericolais et al. *(1997)*

river terraces are, of course, not directly comparable, since the latter once extended for many kilometres offshore, having formed during periods of low sea-level, whereas the beaches relate to the high sea-levels of interglacial optima (Bates this volume). However, the raised beaches are measured above modern sea-level and the terraces above the modern Solent valley floor, which (in the Bournemouth area) is a few metres below modern sea-level (Figure 3.4). Furthermore, both the beaches and the terraces form staircases that are thought to record regional uplift (Preece *et al.* 1990; Bowen 1994; Maddy 1997), the Solent having repeatedly incised its valley in response to this crustal elevation, whereas interglacial sea-level maxima are believed to reflect approximately similar global ocean volumes, so the heights of raised beaches are also a measure of uplift. This means that comparison, based on height, between the raised beach and Solent terrace staircase is perfectly reasonable.

EVOLUTION OF SOLENT DRAINAGE

The Palaeolithic evidence from the Solent gravels provides a potential line of evidence for correlating the isolated terrace sequence to the west of Poole Harbour with that to the east. As noted, the West Knighton Gravel of Allen & Gibbard (1993) is the source of the great majority of palaeoliths in the western area, inviting correlation with the Taddiford Farm Gravel of the Bournemouth area. As Bridgland (1996) noted, it is impossible to link the gravels of the two isolated areas satisfactorily by projecting their longitudinal profiles across Poole Harbour. Indeed,

the greater gradient of the gravels in the Frome catchment and the depth to which the valley floor is excavated (Figure 3.3) both suggest that separate river systems are represented, with separate outlets to the English Channel River. This is very much reinforced by the Palaeolithic evidence (Bridgland 1996). Only the highest surviving gravels in the Frome catchment, which have shallower downstream gradients (Figure 3.3), could conceivably result from headwater drainage of the Solent River system. As noted above, Bridgland (1996) concluded that the Frome was draining southwards to the west of the Needles, and not into the Solent, by the Middle Pleistocene. This view has been supported by the mapping of a substantial submerged, southward-draining palaeo-valley system beneath the sea floor in this area (Velegrakis *et al.* 1999; Figure 3.6). The occurrence of Jurassic chert in the Solent terraces gravels (Allen & Gibbard 1993) suggests that the river once had headwaters in south Dorset, but the long profile projections in Figure 3.3 indicate that this must have been as long ago as the Early Pleistocene, long before human occupation of the valley.

It has been established that the main Solent terrace system, as represented in the Bournemouth–Southampton area, has the largest number of terraces of any river in Britain. To attempt an explanation of this it is necessary to examine theories of terrace formation. As stated above, the fluvial incision that leads to terrace formation is believed to be a response to uplift. The conversion of the uplift, which is probably a progressive and consistent process, into the sporadic formation of aggradational river terraces, has been linked to Pleistocene climatic fluctuation. The repeated oscillation between glacial and

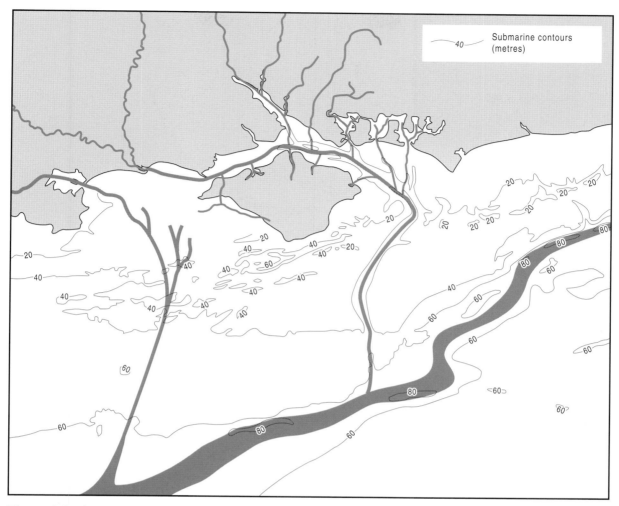

Figure 3.6: the pre-Holocene Solent River system, modified from Bridgland (1996) to incorporate data from Velegrakis et al. (1999)

interglacial climate during the past million years or so is believed, through the influence it has on fluvial activity (particularly discharge and sediment load), to have brought about the alternation of downcutting and aggradation that is recorded in terrace staircases.

Empirical evidence from the Lower Thames sequence, where the river seems to have formed terraces in complete synchrony with the 100Ka interglacial–glacial climatic cycle since the Anglian Stage, was used by Bridgland (1994; Bridgland & Allen 1996) to erect a four-phase model for terrace formation. This evolved into five (Bridgland 1995) and six-phase models, the latter (Bridgland 2000) being reproduced here as Figure 3.7A. The most important element of the model is that the incision that causes a new terrace to form occurs at the ends of glacials, on the warming limb of the climatic cycle (Bridgland & Maddy 1995). This coincides with high discharge from melting permafrost, enabling the river to erode its valley floor, compensating for the uplift that has occurred during the glacial. A second phase of erosion is identified, on the cooling limb (phase 4), but a new terrace does not form because there has

been insufficient uplift during the (briefer) interglacial. The aggradation of the valley floor that follows this second phase of erosion may, however, not reach the full height achieved during the earlier phases of aggradation, as suggested by the relation of phase 2 & 3 to phase 5 deposits within the terrace formations of the Lower Thames (cf. Bridgland 1994, Figures 4.23 and 4.25).

The altitudinal disposition of the Middle Pleistocene terraces of the Solent is suggestive of pairing (Bates this volume; Figure 3.4), with pairs of relatively poorly separated terraces more widely separated from adjacent pairs. It is tempting to suggest that both erosion phases in the terrace model are reflected in this sequence, with the wider separation between pairs, accommodating uplift during the glacials, coinciding with phase 1 and the narrower separation within pairs, corresponding to the uplift during the shorter interglacials, with phase 4. A version of the model redesigned to explain this part of the Solent sequence appears in Figure 3.7B.

Figure 3.4 shows three clear terrace pairs, made up from the Setley Plain/Mount Pleasant, the Old Milton/

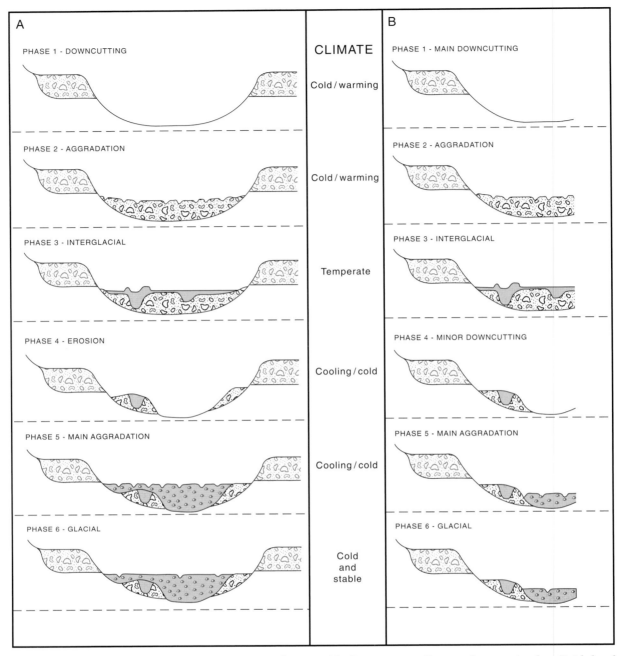

Figure 3.7: formation of river terraces in synchrony with Quaternary climate change: A after Bridgland (2000), B modified to explain the Solent sequence, in which two terraces have been formed in each 100Ka climatic cycle

Tom's Down and the Taddiford Farm/Stanswood Bay Gravels. Fitting of these to the modified climatic terrace model, using the archaeological age indicators discussed above, places the intra pair cooling-limb incision events at the OIS 13–12, 11–10 and 9–8 transitions (Figure 3.3). The downcutting episodes separating these pairs are the normal warming-limb incision events, recognized in other systems, that occurred at the OIS 12–11 and 10–9 transitions. This interpretation is fully compatible with the attribution of the assemblage from the Old Milton Gravel, with twisted ovates, to OIS 11. Downcutting from this

terrace level to the Tom's Down Gravel level is ascribed, in this scheme, to the end of OIS 11, as the colder climate of OIS 10 took hold. At the end of OIS 10 downcutting from the Tom's Down to Taddiford Farm terrace levels took place. The river remained at this level until the climatic deterioration at the end of OIS 9, when it incised to the Stanswood Bay level. The appearance in the Taddiford Farm Gravel of Levallois technique, recognized in Thames assemblages that are thought to date from the earliest part of OIS 8 (see above), thus conforms with this scheme. It does, however, suggest that Levallois technique was in use in Britain very early within OIS 8, perhaps even by the end of OIS 9. There is little evidence with which to date the earlier pair of terraces, made up of the Setley Plain and Mount Pleasant formations, but the attribution of the intra-pair incision event separating these terraces to the OIS 13–12 transition is fully compatible with the elevation of the OIS 13 raised beach at Boxgrove (Figure 3.4).

The lowest three Solent terraces appear to be well separated, suggesting that by the end of the Middle Pleistocene the Solent was forming only single terraces each 100Ka climatic cycle. However, with OIS 7 and 5e recognized within the lowest two terraces, the Lepe and Pennington formations respectively (Figure 3.4; see above), there remains the Milford-on-Sea Gravel to fit into the OIS framework. As downcutting from the Stanswood Bay Terrace to the Milford-on-Sea Terrace would, according to the scheme described above, be attributable to the OIS 8–7 (warming limb) transition, the occurrence of the Lepe interglacial deposits in the terrace below the Milford-on-Sea Gravel poses something of a difficulty. A possible explanation lies in the complexity of OIS 7 as recognized within the marine record. According to Antoine (1994), the Somme, in northern France, formed two terraces in association with separate OIS 7 climatic optima, making this the only oxygen isotope stage to be represented by a pair of terraces in that valley. A similar interpretation of the Milford-on-Sea and Lepe Terraces is appealing, but it would imply that the temperate-climate sediments at Stone Point represent interglacial conditions late in OIS 7. Bridgland & Schreve (in press), however, found that the (admittedly limited) mammalian evidence from Stone Point favoured the earliest woodland phase of OIS 7. Either way, no reliable artefact records can be identified for Solent gravels later than the Milford-on-Sea Formation. Nothing seems to have been recorded from the Lepe Gravel. This is perhaps more in keeping with an OIS 7a interpretation for the Stone Point interglacial deposits. The overlying Lepe Upper Gravel would then be attributable to OIS 6, when humans are thought to have evacuated the British peninsula. The failure of the Lepe Lower Gravel and the Stone Point interglacial sediments to produce artefacts may well relate to their outcrop on the modern foreshore, where there has been little opportunity for their frequent observation.

CONCLUSIONS

The Solent River system is seen as one of the largest and oldest in the British Isles, despite its absence from modern-day maps. Largely drowned by the Holocene marine transgression, it has left an impressive sequence of gravel terraces that, with the addition of tributary gravels, cover a large area of southern England. The Solent almost certainly once drained the Isle of Purbeck, but the Frome, which now drains that area into Poole Harbour, had become a separate tributary of the English Channel River before the beginning of the Middle Pleistocene, its offshore course extending southwards to the west of the Isle of Wight.

The separation of the Frome from the Solent had certainly taken place before humans occupied the Hampshire Basin. That occupation began in the early Middle Pleistocene, as evidenced by the archaeological remains excavated from the Boxgrove raised beach. The distribution of archaeological evidence together with aspects of artefact typology, notably the appearance of twisted ovate handaxes and of Levallois flakes and cores, provide the only evidence from which the ages of the Middle Pleistocene terraces can be judged, save for the interglacial sediments at Stone Point, Lepe. By the Late Pleistocene these hominids had gone, perhaps to return as Neanderthal people fabricating Mousterian tools, but if this was the case there is scant evidence for it from the Solent River. Indeed, the story from there, as with other rivers such as the Thames, is one of prolonged occupation by hominids who left artefacts that show few technological advances during a period of more than 300,000 years. Only the twisted ovates and the Levallois technique appeared to break the monotony!

ACKNOWLEDGEMENTS

The illustrations were prepared by Chris Orton, David Hume and Steven Allan in the Department of Geography at Durham. Funding was received from the Leverhulme Trust (1997–2000) on the project "Middle Pleistocene mammalian biostratigraphy of northwest European rivers". This paper is a contribution to International Geological Correlation Programme project IGCP 449 "Global Correlation of Late Cenozoic fluvial deposits", of which the author is a co-leader.

REFERENCES

Allen, L.G. 1991. *The evolution of the Solent River system during the Pleistocene*. Unpublished Ph.D. thesis, University of Cambridge.

Allen, L.G. & Gibbard, P.L. 1993. Pleistocene evolution of the Solent River of southern England. *Quaternary Science Reviews* 12: 503–528.

Allen, L.G., Gibbard, P.L., Pettitt, M.E., Preece, R.C. & Robinson, J.E. 1996. Late Pleistocene deposits at Pennington Marshes, Lymington, Hampshire, Southern England. *Proceedings of the Geologists' Association* 107: 39–50.

Antoine, P. 1994. The Somme valley terrace system (northern France): a model of river response to Quaternary climatic variations since 800,000 bp. *Terra*

Nova 6: 453–464.

Arkell, W.J. 1947. *The Geology of the Country around Weymouth, Swanage, Corfe and Lulworth*. Memoir of the British Geological Survey, Sheets 341–343. HMSO, London.

Ashton, N.M., Cook, J., Lewis, S.G. & Rose, J. (ed's) 1992. *High Lodge: excavations by G. de G. Sieveking, 1962–8 and J. Cook, 1988*. British Museum Press, London.

Barber, K.E. & Brown, A.G. 1987. Late Pleistocene organic deposits beneath the floodplain of the River Avon at Ibsley, Hampshire. In K.E. Barber (ed.) *Wessex and the Isle of Wight: Field Guide*: 65–74. Quaternary Research Association, Cambridge.

Bates, M.R., Parfitt, S.A. and Roberts, M.B. 1998. Later Middle and Upper Pleistocene sediments of the West Sussex coastal plain: a brief review. In J.B. Murton, C.A. Whiteman, M.R. Bates, D.R. Bridgland, A.J. Long, M.B. Roberts & M.P. Waller (ed's) *The Quaternary of Kent and Sussex: Field Guide*: 151–165. Quaternary Research Association, London.

Bishop, M.J. 1982. The mammal fauna of the early Middle Pleistocene cavern infill site of Westbury-sub-Mendip, Somerset. *Special Papers in Palaeontology* 28: 1–108.

Bowen, D.Q. 1994. Late Cenozoic Wales and South-West England. *Proceedings of the Ussher Society* 8: 209–213.

Bridgland, D.R. 1994. *Quaternary of the Thames*. Geological Conservation Review Series 7. Chapman and Hall, London.

Bridgland, D.R. 1995. The Quaternary sequence of the eastern Thames basin: problems of correlation. In D.R. Bridgland, P. Allen & B.A. Haggart (ed's) *The Quaternary of the Lower Reaches of the Thames: Field Guide*: 35–52. Quaternary Research Association, Durham.

Bridgland, D.R. 1996. Quaternary river terrace deposits as a framework for the Lower Palaeolithic record. In C.S. Gamble & A.J. Lawson (ed's) *The English Palaeolithic Reviewed*: 23–39. Wessex Archaeology, Salisbury.

Bridgland, D.R. 1998. The Pleistocene history and early human occupation of the River Thames valley. In N. Ashton, F. Healy & P. Pettitt (ed's) *Stone Age Archaeology: Essays in honour of John Wymer*: 29–37. Lithic Studies Society Occasional Paper 6. Oxbow Books, Oxford.

Bridgland, D.R. 2000. River terrace systems in north-west Europe: an archive of environmental change, uplift and early human occupation. *Quaternary Science Reviews* 19: 1293–1303.

Bridgland, D.R. & Allen, P. 1996. A revised model for terrace formation and its significance for the lower Middle Pleistocene Thames terrace aggradations of north-east Essex, U.K. In C. Turner (ed.) *The Early Middle Pleistocene in Europe*: 121–134. Balkema, Rotterdam.

Bridgland, D.R. and Maddy, D. 1995. River terraces as records of Quaternary climate oscillation. *Programme with Abstracts*: 37. INQUA XIV, Berlin.

Bridgland, D.R. & Schreve, D.C. (in press). River terrace formation in synchrony with long-term climatic fluctuation: examples from southern Britain. In D. Maddy, M. Macklin & J. Woodward (ed's) *River Basin Sediments Systems: Archives of Environmental Change*. Balkema, Rotterdam.

Bristow, C.R., Freshney, E.C. & Penn, I.E. 1991. *Geology of the Country around Bournemouth*. Memoir of the British Geological Survey, Sheet 329. HMSO, London.

Brown, R.C., Gilbertson, D.D., Green, C.P. & Keen, D.H. 1975. Stratigraphy and environmental significance of Pleistocene deposits at Stone, Hampshire. *Proceedings of the Geologists' Association* 86: 349–363.

Bury, H. 1923. Some aspects of the Hampshire plateau gravels. *Proceedings of the Prehistoric Society of East Anglia* 4: 15–41.

Evans, J. 1872, 1st edition. *The Ancient Stone Implements, Weapons and Ornaments of Great Britain*. Longmans, Green & Co., London.

Evans, J. 1897, 2nd edition. *The Ancient Stone Implements, Weapons and Ornaments of Great Britain*. Longmans, Green & Co., London.

Everard, C.E. 1954. "The Solent River" a geomorphological study. *Transactions of the Institute of British Geographers* 20: 41–58.

Fox, W.D. 1862. When and how was the Isle of Wight separated from the mainland? *Geologist* 5: 452.

Gibbard, P.L. 1994. *Pleistocene History of the Lower Thames Valley*. Cambridge University Press, Cambridge.

Gibbard, P.L. & Allen, L.G. 1994. Drainage evolution in south and east England during the Pleistocene. *Terra Nova* 6: 444–452.

Gibbard, P.L. & Preece, R.C. 1999. South and Southeast England. In D.Q. Bowen (ed.) *A Revised Correlation of Quaternary Deposits in the British Isles*: 59–65. Geological Society of London, Special Report No. 23. Geological Society, Bath.

Green, C.P. and Keen, D.H., 1987. Stratigraphy and palaeoenvironments of the Stone Point deposits: the 1975 investigation. In K.E. Barber (ed.) *Wessex and the Isle of Wight: Field Guide*: 17–20. Quaternary Research Association, Cambridge.

Hamblin, R.J.O., Crosby, A., Balson, P.S., Jones, S.M., Chadwick, R.A., Penn, I.E. & Arthur, M.J. 1992. *The Geology of the English Channel*. British Geological Survey, United Kingdom Offshore Regional Report. HMSO, London.

Hollin, J.T. 1977. Thames interglacial sites, Ipswichian sea levels and Antarctic ice surges. *Boreas* 6: 33–52.

Hosfield, R.T. 1999. *The Palaeolithic of the Hampshire Basin*. British Archaeological Reports, British Series, No. 286. Archaeopress, Oxford.

King, W.B.R. & Oakley, K.P. 1936. The Pleistocene succession in the lower part of the Thames Valley. *Proceedings of the Prehistoric Society* 1: 52–76.

Lericolais G., Auffret J.P. & Bourillet J.F. 1997. *Evolution plio-quaternaire du fleuve Manche: Stratigraphie et Géomorphologie de la confluence de la Paléo-Somme et de la Paléo-Seine*. Unpublished conference abstract, Association des Sedimentologues de France, Montpellier.

Maddy, D. 1997. Uplift-driven valley incision and river terrace formation in southern England. *Journal of Quaternary Science* 12: 539–545.

Nicholls, R.J. 1987. Evolution of the upper reaches of the Solent River and the formation of Poole and Christchurch Bays. In K.E. Barber (ed.) *Wessex and the Isle of Wight: Field Guide*: 99–114. Quaternary Research Association, Cambridge.

Preece, R.C. 1995. Mollusca from interglacial sediments at three critical sites in the Lower Thames. In D.R. Bridgland, P. Allen, & B.A. Haggart (ed's) *The Quaternary of the lower reaches of the Thames: Field Guide*: 55–60. Quaternary Research Association,

Durham.

Preece, R.C. 1999. Mollusca from the Last interglacial fluvial deposits at Trafalgar Square, London. *Journal of Quaternary Science* 14: 77–89.

Preece, R.C. and Parfitt, S.A. 2000. The Cromer Forest-bed: new thoughts on an old problem. In S.G. Lewis, C.A. Whiteman & R.C. Preece (ed's) *The Quaternary of Norfolk and Suffolk: Field Guide*: 1–27. Quaternary Research Association, London,

Preece, R.C., Scourse, J.D., Houghton, S., Knudsen, K.L. and Penney, D.N. 1990. The Pleistocene sea-level and neotectonic history of the eastern Solent, southern England. *Philosophical Transactions of the Royal Society of London Series B 328*: 315–333.

Reid, C. 1893. A fossiliferous deposit at Stone, on the Hampshire coast. *Quarterly Journal of the Geological Society of London* 49: 325–329.

Reid, C. 1902. *The geology of the country around Ringwood.* Memoir of the British Geological Survey, Sheet 314. HMSO, London.

Reynolds, P.J. 1987. Lepe Cliff: the evidence for a pre-Devensian brickearth. In K.E. Barber (ed.) *Wessex and the Isle of Wight: Field Guide*: 21–22. Quaternary Research Association, Cambridge.

Roberts, M.B. 1986. Excavation of the Lower Palaeolithic site at Amey's Eartham Pit, Boxgrove, West Sussex: a preliminary report. *Proceedings of the Prehistoric Society* 52: 215–245.

Roberts, M.B., Stringer, C.B. & Parfitt, S.A. 1994. A hominid tibia from Middle Pleistocene sediments at Boxgrove, U.K. *Nature* 369: 311–313.

Roe, D.A. 1968. British Lower and Middle Palaeolithic handaxe groups. *Proceedings of the Prehistoric Society* 34: 1–81.

Schreve, D.C. 1997. *Mammalian Biostratigraphy of the Later Middle Pleistocene in Britain.* Unpublished Ph.D. thesis, University of London.

Small, R.J. 1964. Geomorphology. In F.J. Monkhouse (ed.) *A survey of Southampton and its region*: 37–50. Southampton University Press, Southampton.

Velegrakis, A.F., Dix, J.K. & Collins, M.B. 1999. Late Quaternary evolution of the upper reaches of the Solent River, Southern England, based upon marine geophysical evidence. *Journal of the Geological Society of London* 156: 73–87.

Wessex Archaeology. 1993. *The Upper Thames valley, the Kennet valley and the Solent drainage system.* The Southern Rivers Palaeolithic Project, Report No. 1. Wessex Archaeology, Salisbury.

West, I.M. 1980. Geology of the Solent estuarine system. In NERC *The Solent Estuarine System*: 6–19. NERC Publication, Series C, No. 22. NERC, Swindon.

West, R.G. 1969. Pollen analyses from interglacial deposits at Aveley and Grays, Essex. *Proceedings of the Geologists' Association* 80: 271–282.

West, R.G. 1987. Interglacial deposits at Stone Point: the 1960 investigation. In K.E. Barber (ed.) *Wessex and the Isle of Wight: Field Guide*: 15–16. Quaternary Research Association, Cambridge.

West, R.G. & Sparks, B.W. 1960. Coastal interglacial deposits of the English Channel. *Philosophical Transactions of the Royal Society of London Series B* 243: 95–133.

White, M.J. 1998. Twisted ovate bifaces in the British Lower Palaeolithic. In N. Ashton, F. Healy & P. Pettitt (ed's) *Stone Age Archaeology: Essays in Honour of John Wymer*: 98–104. Lithic Studies Society Occasional Paper 6. Oxbow Books, Oxford.

Wymer, J.J. 1988. Palaeolithic archaeology and the British Quaternary sequence. *Quaternary Science Reviews* 7: 79–98.

Wymer, J.J. 1999. *The Lower Palaeolithic occupation of Britain.* Wessex Archaeology and English Heritage, Salisbury.

4. THE MEETING OF THE WATERS: RAISED BEACHES AND RIVER GRAVELS OF THE SUSSEX COASTAL PLAIN/HAMPSHIRE BASIN

M.R. Bates

ABSTRACT

Integrating Pleistocene sediments from continental systems and the marine stratigraphic record is a key objective for Quaternary science. In many cases correlation of these records is only possible through comparison of proxy records. However, this objective may be realised in those areas of the world where marine marginal sediments occur in close proximity to terrestrial fluvial deposits in the lower reaches of major river valleys. One such location is the Sussex/Hampshire corridor in southern England. Pleistocene sediments within the area of the former Solent River system and the West Sussex Coastal Plain are evidence for a wide variety of different depositional systems ranging from temperate floodplains and marine beaches to cold climate braided river channels. These deposits may contain archaeological material such as handaxes as well as faunal and floral remains. The proximity of sediments of both temperate and cold climate types within the lower reaches of the modern major river valleys should allow correlation between the temperate and cold climate stratigraphic records in this area. This evidence may be used to link the marine and fluvial stratigraphic records. This paper describes the nature of the different types of evidence from the Sussex/Hampshire corridor and considers some of the problems and pitfalls in the use of this information in the construction of an integrated stratigraphic framework for the area.

INTRODUCTION

The Sussex/Hampshire corridor describes an area of southern England extending from Brighton in the east to Poole Harbour in the west and from the Isle of Wight in the south northwards to Southampton and beyond. This area is rich in unconsolidated sediments dating to the Pleistocene Epoch that have been known to contain archaeological material since the first recorded discoveries in the 19th century (Wessex Archaeology 1994; Bates *et al.* 1997; Hosfield 1999).

The regional topography, the nature of the Pleistocene history and the predominant sediment types present in the area suggest that three distinct regions can be recognised within the corridor:

- The West Sussex Coastal Plain, from Brighton to Portsmouth, dominated by marine deposits overlain by periglacial sediments (Bates, Parfitt & Roberts 1997).
- The Poole/Portsmouth area dominated by fluvial sediments of the former Solent River (Everard 1954; Allen & Gibbard 1993; Gibbard & Allen 1994; Bridgland 1996, this volume).
- The Sussex Rivers (Arun and Adur) area where fluvial sediments lie within valleys entering the coastal plain area from the Weald.

The history and conditions of sediment deposition within these three areas have varied. Fluvial sediments, deposited under predominantly cold climate, periglacial conditions during phases of lowered sea levels alternated with marine sediments deposited during temperate high sea level events.

Correlation between elements of these diverse depositional systems is difficult due to the incompatibility of the time frames and depositional events responsible for sequence formation. However,

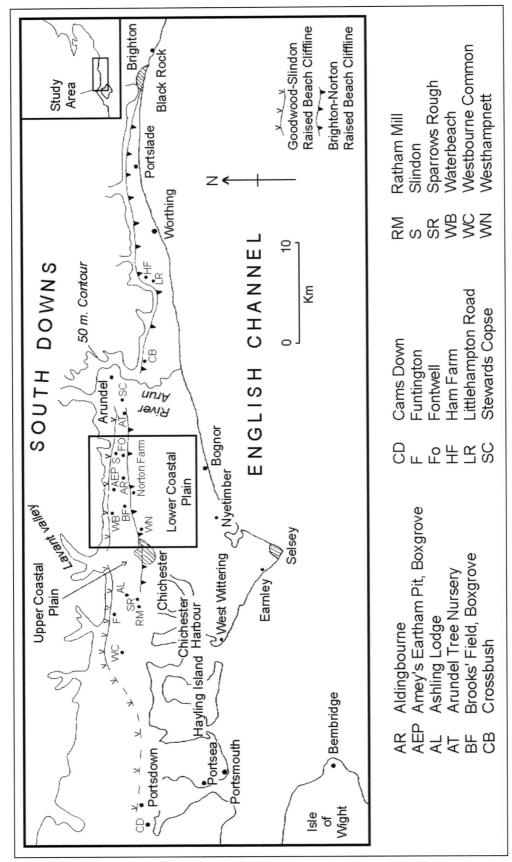

Figure 4.1: site location plan for the West Sussex Coastal Plain showing the location of the main sites described in the text and the positions of the Goodwood–Slindon and Brighton–Norton cliff lines

the opportunity exists within the area to begin to investigate the relationship between these diverse depositional systems, e.g. where sequence types overlap within the areas at the confluence of the fluvial and marine sequences such as former estuaries.

INTERGLACIAL SHALLOW MARINE AND TERRESTRIAL SEQUENCES OF THE WEST SUSSEX COASTAL PLAIN

Temperate sediments from marine or marine marginal situations are well known and described from numerous sites within the West Sussex Coastal Plain area (Bates *et al.* 1997; Figure 4.1). These deposits consist of clastic shoreface sediments (including beach gravels and inter-tidal/sub-tidal sands), estuarine or lagoonal sands and silts and overlying terrestrial and low-energy fluvial clays and silts. Typically these sediments were deposited during temperate conditions associated with the maximum phase of sea level rise or, more probably, during a phase of falling relative sea level prior to the onset of the cold climate periglacial conditions in the succeeding cold phase.

Shallow marine sequences

Early observations, drawing attention to the presence of marine sediments elevated above present day sea level, on the West Sussex Coastal Plain, were made by Prestwich (1859). Further observations were published by Prestwich in 1892 in an article in which he attempted to correlate the deposits from Sussex with similar deposits elsewhere in Southern Britain. However it was only in the early 20th century that researchers determined that more than one high sea-level event had occurred in the area (Palmer & Cooke 1923; Fowler 1932; Calkin 1934). This work suggested that two, altitudinally discrete beaches were present (Fowler 1932) consisting of an upper series of sands and gravels at heights above 30m (100 feet) O.D. (Ordnance Datum) and a lower series of sands and gravels at 4.5m (15 feet) O.D. on the lower coastal plain. Later workers suggested an Hoxnian (Holsteinian) age for the highest 30m raised beach (Shephard-Thorn & Kellaway 1978) and an Ipswichian (last interglacial / Eemian) age for the lower raised beach (West & Sparks 1960; Hodgson 1964).

Recently the sedimentary evidence from the area has been augmented by extensive works undertaken by the British Geological Survey as part of the remapping of the area and mineral aggregate sand and gravel evaluations (Berry & Shephard-Thorn 1982; Shephard-Thorn, Berry & Wyatt 1982; Bristow & Wyatt 1983; Lovell & Nancarrow 1983; Young & Lake 1988). This data suggested that a revision of the Quaternary stratigraphy within the area was necessary

and consequently the number and distribution of discrete high sea level events recognised in the area has now been increased (Bates *et al.* 1997; Figure 4.2, Table 4.1).

At present at least four altitudinally and temporally distinct sequences of raised marine sediments can be identified within the area to the east of Chichester (Figure 4.2). Typically these sequences consist of well-stratified rounded beach gravels in the vicinity of the palaeo-cliffline and stratified sands (often containing marine bivalves and ichnofossils – e.g. see Colcutt 1999). Three of these have been defined and mapped across the coastal plain and consist of the Goodwood–Slindon Beach, Aldingbourne Raised Beach and Brighton–Norton Raised Beach (Bates *et al.* 1997). The status of sediments south of the known outcrop of the Brighton–Norton Raised Beach is less clear. Gravels around Selsey Bill have been ascribed to the Pagham Formation (Pagham Raised Beach) but their inland distribution and relationship with the Brighton–Norton Raised Beach remains equivocal.

These marine sediments may be traced across a wide area of the coastal plain from Portsdown and Bembridge in the west to Brighton in the east (Figure 4.1). Presently no known exposures of marine sediments exist to the west of Portsdown and with the exception of a few observations little has been written of these deposits at the extreme western end of the corridor.

Channel fill sequences of the Selsey Peninsula

Other types of sediments related to sea level highstand phases include the fossiliferous sediments infilling shallow channels around Selsey Bill (Reid 1903). These channel deposits have been described by many authors including Reid (1892), Heron-Allen (1911), Palmer & Cooke (1923), West & Sparks (1960) and West *et al.* (1984). These channels, cut into Tertiary bedrock, sometimes contain brackish water faunas and are present in the area lying at or below current sea-level between Selsey and West Wittering (Figure 4.1). The deposits appear to be stratified below raised beach deposits in some cases (Reid 1892; West & Sparks 1960; West *et al.* 1984; Stinton 1985) and have been ascribed ages varying from the early Middle Pleistocene (West *et al.* 1984) to Ipswichian (West & Sparks 1960).

Investigation of these deposits has been piecemeal and in certain instances conflicting evidence has been generated from different specialist works. For example study of the Lifeboat Station channel at Selsey (West & Sparks 1960) indicated infilling of the channel under transgressive conditions during a phase of rising relative sea level. However Whatley & Kaye (1971) suggest that foraminifera from the same sediment units implied infilling of the channel under

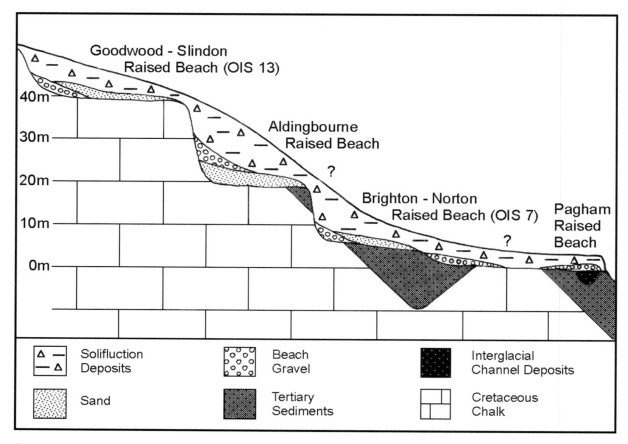

Figure 4.2: schematic profile showing the main identified raised beach sequences of the West Sussex Coastal Plain and the relationship with the Marine Oxygen Isotope Stratigraphic record

regressive conditions. This apparent contradiction may be resolved by consideration of the nature of the channels themselves and their infilling within the interglacial phases.

Comparison of the size of these channels (typically less than three metres deep) with Holocene channels currently existing to the east and west of Selsey Bill (e.g. the Arun Valley Holocene fills may exceed 20m in thickness) indicate that all of the infilled channels around Selsey Bill are considerably smaller and shallower than those of the main Holocene infilled valleys. The smaller Pleistocene channels would have infilled under very different conditions to the deeper channels, such as that of the Arun, in which a thicker sequence (of considerable time depth) recording a large part of the interglacial succession built up. The smaller Pleistocene channels are therefore likely to only contain short sequences within the interglacial and probably existed in ephemeral locations relative to the main contemporary channels recording the main transgressive/regressive signatures of the interglacial. The channels around the Bill could therefore be viewed as channels infilled, perhaps quite rapidly, when a threshold had been reached in sea level rise and main valley fills. Given the low gradient of these channels and the shifting nature of sedimentation patterns in the lower parts of

such marine marginal situations changes in patterns of sedimentation at the mouth of the channels may easily have led to local transgressive/regressive trends superimposed on the longer term transgressive/regressive trends of the interglacial. Consequently the significance of the apparent trends in marine transgression/regression within these shallow channels should be treated with caution.

Terrestrial sediments

Temperate terrestrial sediments are often present above the marine regressive phase sediments within the area. Often these sediments overlie a buried landsurface on which faunal remains and sometimes, archaeological material may exist, e.g. at Boxgrove (Roberts & Parfitt 1999). These terrestrial sediments are typically very low energy fluvial deposits forming under slow moving water in ponds or 'lacustrine' sediments forming in temporary standing water bodies. In some cases, e.g. at Norton Farm, these deposits belong to a phase of deteriorating climate containing a sequence of buried soils or weathering horizons (Bates *et al.* 2000).

The marine/terrestrial sediments, such as those at Boxgrove and Norton Farm are usually overlain or cut through by a sequence of coarse flint gravels

Height Distributions	Geographical Zone	Group	Formation (Member)	Member (Beds) (informal)	Inferred Environments of Deposition
			PAGHAM (Pagham Raised Beach)	Pagham Gravel	Inter-tidal marine marginal
Low Level Deposits -2.0 – +3.0m O.D			WEST WITTERING		Freshwater to estuarine transgressional channel
			LIFE BOAT STATION		Freshwater to estuarine transgressional channel
			EARNLEY		Estuarine regressional channel
	LOWER COASTAL PLAIN	LOWER COASTAL PLAIN	CHICHESTER		Cold climate fluvial gravels
Low Level Deposits +5.0 – +12.0 m O.D.			NYTON		Cold climate periglacial solifluction gravels and silts
			NORTON (Brighton–Norton Raised Beach)	Norton Silts Norton Sands	Terrestrial–estuarine Inter/sub-tidal marine
Intermediate Level Deposits +15.0 – +18.0m O.D.			CAMS DOWN (Cams Down Raised Beach)	[Cams Down–Ratham Mill–Sparrows Rough Deposits]	[Inter-tidal marine marginal]
Intermediate Level Deposits +17.5 – +27.5m O.D.	**UPPER COASTAL PLAIN**	UPPER COASTAL PLAIN	ALDINGBOURNE (Aldingbourne Raised Beach)	Aldingbourne Gravel Aldingbourne Sand	Inter-tidal marine marginal Inter/sub-tidal marine
			EARTHAM	Eartham Upper Gravel Eartham Lower Gravel	Cold climate periglacial solifluction gravels and silts
Higher Level Deposits +32.0 – +43.0m O.D.			SLINDON (Goodwood–Slindon Raised Beach)	Slindon Silt Slindon Sand Slindon Gravel	Terrestrial–estuarine Inter/sub-tidal marine Inter-tidal marine marginal

Table 4.1: chronostratigraphy and lithostratigraphy of the main sequences in the area of the West Sussex Coastal Plain

deposited under periglacial conditions. These deposits formed either as solifucted masses of material derived from the decaying cliff or the South Downs, as at Boxgrove (Roberts & Parfitt 1999) or as a series of fluvially-deposited sediments derived from the dry valley systems developed within the South Downs, e.g. the Chichester Fan Gravels. In some instances the sediments derived from the South Downs may contain fine grained sediment sequences developed in abandoned channels that may be rich in floral and faunal remains, e.g. at Portfield Pit, Westhampnett East (Bates 1998).

At present there is no conclusive evidence for high sea level stand temperate fluvial floodplain sediments associated with the larger river systems within the area of the coastal plain.

FLUVIAL SEDIMENTS OF THE SOLENT RIVER SYSTEM

Sediments within the area to the west of Portsmouth belong to a major river system, named the Solent River (Darwin-Fox 1862), and deposits consist of coarse flint gravels laid down by rivers operating under cold climate conditions with high discharge rates that were graded to base levels considerably below that of the present day. The deposits are particularly well developed within the area to the west of the Solent where the sands and gravels have been associated with a major west to east flowing river (Allen & Gibbard 1993; Figure 4.3). These coarse cold climate deposits sometimes contain beds of finer-grained floodplain and estuarine silts that may contain floral and faunal elements, e.g. at Ibsley (Barber & Brown 1987), Pennington (Allen *et al.* 1996) and Stone Point, Lepe (Brown *et al.* 1975).

Sub-division of the deposits of the western Solent system (Table 4.2) is complex and a number of different aggradational sequences, some underlying morphological terraces, exist in the area (Allen & Gibbard 1993; Gibbard & Allen 1994; Bridgland 1996). Similar gravels exist on the eastern edge of the Solent where BGS mapping has identified 11 morphological terraces (Edwards & Freshney 1987; Table 4.2). However at present it is not possible to relate the eastern sequences of morphological terraces (and associated fluvial sediments) identified by the BGS (Edwards & Freshney 1987) with those described by Allen & Gibbard (1993) from the western Solent system.

Fluvial sediments of the former Solent system have been located in off-shore areas and are associated with a series of drowned valley forms

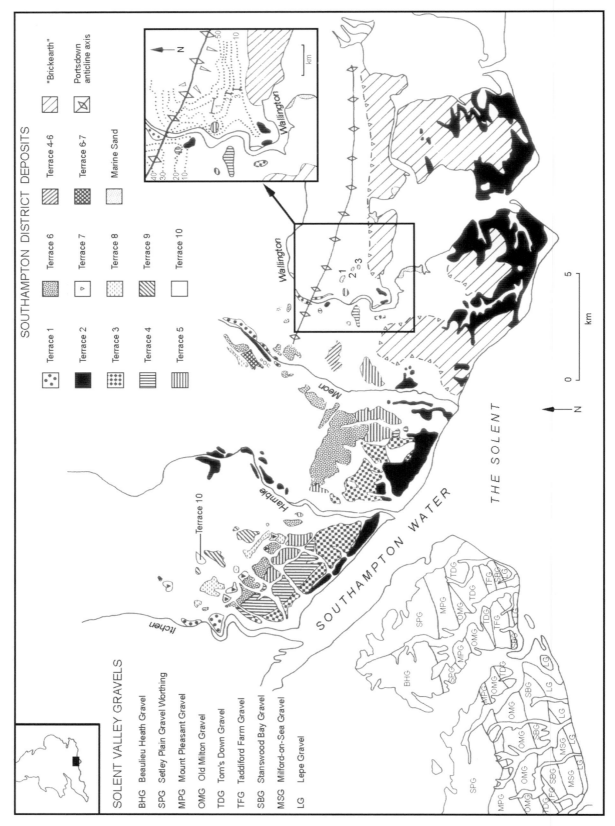

Figure 4.3: distribution of the major gravel bodies of the Solent and Southampton districts (modified from Allen & Gibbard 1993 and Edwards & Freshney 1987); inset shows a contour plot and the distribution of sediments at the eastern end of the Portsdown Anticline

Solent Valley (west)	Solent Valley (east)	Stage	Marine Isotope Stages (sub-Stages)
North End Copse Gravel (Buried Channel deposits)	Buried Channel deposits	Late Devensian	
			2-5b
Pennington Upper Gravel	Terrace 1	Devensian	
Pennington Marshes organic deposits		Ipswichian	5e
Pennington Lower Gravel ?Lepe Upper Gravel	Terrace 2 Terrace 3	Late Saalian	6
Stone Point (Lepe) organic deposits		Intra-Saalian temperate stage	7
Lepe Lower Gravel Milford-on-Sea Gravel	Terrace 4 Terrace 5		
			?9/11
Stanswood Bay Gravel Taddiford Farm Gravel	Terrace 6 Terrace 7		
			?9/11
Tom's Down Gravel Old Milton Gravel	Terrace 8 Terrace 9		
		Pre-Anglian/ Post-Cromerian (ss)	?13
Mount Pleasant Gravel Setley Plain Gravel	Terrace 10 Terrace 11		
			?13
Beaulieu Heath Gravel Tiptoe Gravel Sway Gravel Holmsey Ridge Gravel Whitefield Hill Gravel			

Table 4.2: lithostratigraphic units of the Solent River system

incised into the sea bed (Dyer 1975; West 1980). Within some of these valley forms a series of fluvial sediments are known to be present (Velegrakis *et al.* 1999).

FLUVIAL SEDIMENTS OF THE SUSSEX RIVERS

River valleys to the east of the Solent are considerably smaller than those of the Solent system and have their headwaters within the Weald area to the north of the South Downs. Only two major rivers currently flow through the chalk downland block from the Weald to the channel coast via the West Sussex Coastal Plain; the Arun and Adur. Investigation of the sediments associated with these rivers has been piecemeal and currently little recent investigation of these systems has occurred. Within the Arun system early work from the Weald area was reported by Kirkaldy & Bull (1940) and Thurrell *et al.* (1968) and summarised by Woodcock (1981). Evidence from the river course through the chalk to the sea was described as long ago as the 1930s by Bull (1932, 1936). The Adur system has received even less attention with summarised work by White (1924),

Kirkaldy & Bull (1940) and more recently by Young & Lake (1988). The archaeological material from these river valleys has recently been collated by Wessex Archaeology (1994). It should be noted that the basis for describing and mapping these deposits within the Arun and Adur systems was based on the identification and mapping of terrace surfaces of the river and not on the basis of the distribution of fluvial deposits underlying these morphological features. This contrasts with the lithostratigraphic approach taken by Allen & Gibbard (1993) in the Solent area.

Despite this absence of recent work and the difficulties encountered when attempting to use information that has been generated using a philosophy very different to that presently used to map and interpret fluvial sequences in river valleys it is interesting to note that there appears to be a decrease in numbers of preserved terraces or fluvial aggradations from west to east across the coastal plain (Figure 4.4). Eastwards the numbers of identified terraces and/or fluvial aggradations decrease from in excess of 11 within the eastern Solent (Figure 4.3), seven in the Meon, six in the Wallington and Arun and three in the Adur (Figure 4.4; Gibbard, in prep.). The significance of this pattern will be considered below.

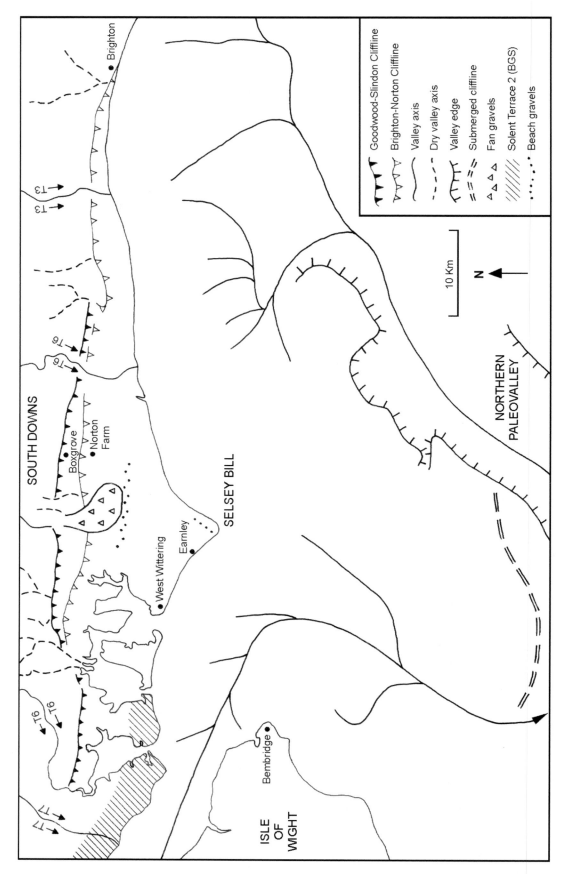

Figure 4.4: major river valleys and their offshore equivalents within the West Sussex Coastal Plain; numbers of mapped river terraces are shown as T7, T6 etc. for individual rivers

Offshore extensions of these Sussex valley systems can be traced into the central English Channel area where, e.g. Bellamy (1995) has described seabed forms for the area south of the Selsey/Arundel area. Both the Solent system and the Sussex rivers can be traced offshore into the Northern Palaeovalley complex — a part of the complex Channel river system (Kellaway *et al.* 1975; Gibbard 1988, 1995; Lautridou *et al.* 1999).

INTEGRATING THE EVIDENCE

Before examining any physical relationship between the different sedimentary systems described above it is necessary to consider the nature of sequence generation within the area. A number of important factors need to be considered prior to formulating a model describing such relationships:

- Marine sediments recovered from the coastal plain area are considered to represent sequences deposited during high sea level stands during or at the end of temperate phases in the Quaternary. Minor differences in recovered biological assemblages from these beaches indicate that some deposits formed during fully temperate episodes, e.g. the sediments of the Slindon Formation at Boxgrove (Roberts & Parfitt 1999), while other deposits appear to have formed under cooling climate conditions at the transition from warm to cold stages, e.g. the sediments recovered from Norton Farm (Bates *et al.* 2000). No evidence exists to suggest that any of these marine sequences are cold climate marine deposits formed during sea level low stands and subsequently uplifted to their present position as has been suggested controversially for some of the late Devensian marine deposits of the Irish Sea (Eyles & MacCabe 1991).
- The major fluvial deposits were formed during phases of lowered sea level during cold climates. During these episodes deposition of gravels during either cooling or warming events either side of the glacial maximum within a cold stage will alternate with phases of downcutting and incision associated with lowered sea level.
- Long term uplift is indicated within the area of the coastal plain. Rates of uplift during the Pleistocene have previously been calculated by Preece *et al.* (1990) and Roberts & Parfitt (1999) for the West Sussex Coastal Plain. The rates calculated by Roberts & Parfitt (1999) agree well with uplift rates calculated from the investigation of fluvial sequences in southern Britain by Maddy (1997). However uplift rates and patterns of uplift in the English Channel area are likely to be complex (e.g. see van Vliet-Lanoë *et al.* 2000). One possible manifestation of this

complexity within the Sussex Coastal Plain area may be reflected in the apparent decrease in numbers of terraces/fluvial aggradations from west to east across the coastal plain noted earlier (Figure 4.4). This pattern may be a result of differential uplift rates across the plain with higher uplift rates in the west compared to the east. However, care should be taken when drawing such conclusions and the antiquity of the data, the length of the river systems and the possible influence of differing bedrock geologies within the river hinterlands may all play a role in determining the number of terraces/fluvial aggradations within these systems.

However, given that the assumptions made above are valid it is possible to propose a model describing the relationship between marine high stand sediments and fluvial low stand sediments within the area at the mouth of a present day river valley system, where fluvial sediments were deposited within a valley where the valley axis moved from east to west (Figure 4.5). This model suggest that a number of phases would be recognised in an area subject to constant uplift:

- *Phase I.* Temperate episode and sea level high stand phase during which deposition of shallow marine and beach sediments occurred during transgression 1.
- *Phase II.* Cold stage episode resulting in falling sea levels and incision through marine sequences by fluvial activity within the area of the former mouth of major river valleys. Deposition of coarse fluvial gravels by the river during this stage. The older marine deposits from the earlier transgression remain isolated as remnants above and adjacent to the valley mouth area of the former estuary. More than 1 phase of fluvial aggradation may occur in this cold stage. Uplift continues through this phase.
- *Phase III.* A return to temperate conditions resulting in a sea level high stand phase during which deposition of shallow marine and beach sediments occurred during transgression 2. Remnants of the older fluvial deposits from the preceding cold stage would exist at datums above the marine sediments associated with transgression 2 due to uplift history.
- *Phase IV.* Further incision and fluvial sediment deposition during the subsequent sea level low stand cold phase. Older sediments from previous depositional episodes remain as remnants above the latest deposits due to uplift and the lateral shift in valley floor centre.

This model therefore predicts that physical relationships should exist between these types of deposits on the coastal plain. Demonstration that such

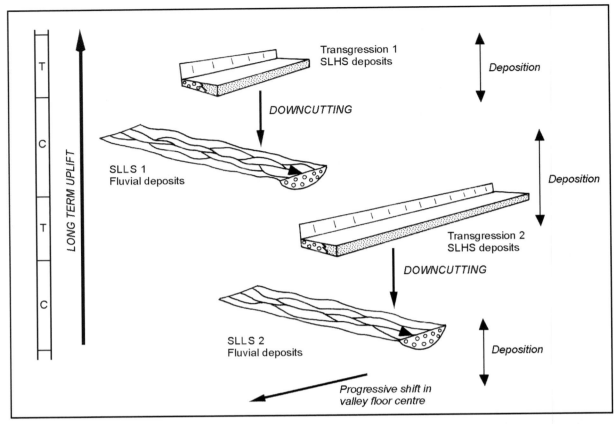

Figure 4.5: conceptual model illustrating the relationship between climate systems, uplift and the nature of sediment deposition at the mouth of major river valleys entering the coastal plain area. Transgression 1, a temperate episode and sea level high stand phase during which deposition of shallow marine and beach sediments occurred. This was followed by downcutting during a cold stage episode caused by falling sea levels (sea level low stand phase 1). Deposition of coarse fluvial gravels occurred during this stage. More than 1 phase of fluvial aggradation may occur in this cold stage. Uplift continues through this phase. Transgression 2 subsequently occurred during a sea level high stand phase following a return to temperate conditions during which deposition of shallow marine and beach sediments occurred. Further downcutting followed during a subsequent sea level low stand and fluvial sediment deposition during the subsequent sea level low stand cold phase. Older sediments were deposited.

relationships do occur would provide the basis for a framework for integrating the river valley sediments of the Weald and Solent systems with the (relatively) well dated sequences of the West Sussex Coastal Plain.

THE PORTSDOWN/GOSPORT CORRIDOR

The Pleistocene sediments of the Portsdown and Gosport (Figures 4.3, 4.6 and 4.7) area fall within the area that would have formed the outer estuary area for the Solent River system of Gibbard & Allen (1994) during sea level high stand phases. This area marks the westernmost extent of the marine sequences that can be traced westwards from the West Sussex Coastal Plain. The area lies to the east of the main eastern Solent gravels mapped by the BGS trending from north west to south east between the Itchen and

Wallington rivers (Figure 4.3).

Marine sediments were first reported from this area by Prestwich (1872) from Down Coppice Gravel Pit (NGR SU 599064; Site 2, Figures 4.6 and 4.7). The sediments at the site consisted of laminated sands and beach gravels resting at elevations in excess of 30 metres O.D. Excavations during the summer of 1999 by the author within the old Down Coppice Gravel Pit (presently a caravan park) failed to reveal any marine sands or gravels in sections cut through the northern and eastern faces of the old quarry. It appears likely that quarrying had removed all vestiges of the commercially viable marine deposits and quarrying ceased when periglacial clay-rich gravels were encountered. However, it was noted that fields immediately to the east of Down Coppice Gravel Pit were rich in well rounded flint cobbles suggesting the presence of stratified sequences below the ploughsoil in these locations.

Further observations of sediments thought to be of

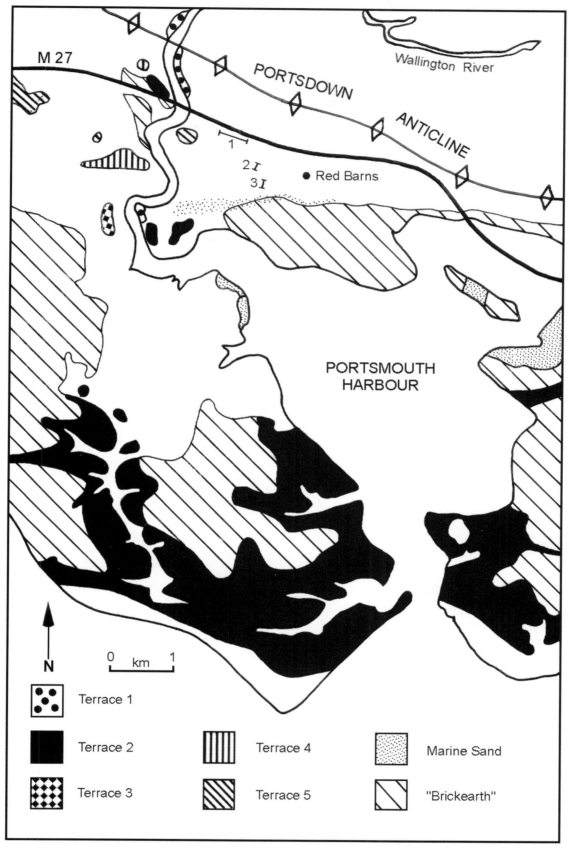

Figure 4.6: location of sediment units and mapped terraces in the Portsdown-Portsmouth corridor (modified from BGS 1998)

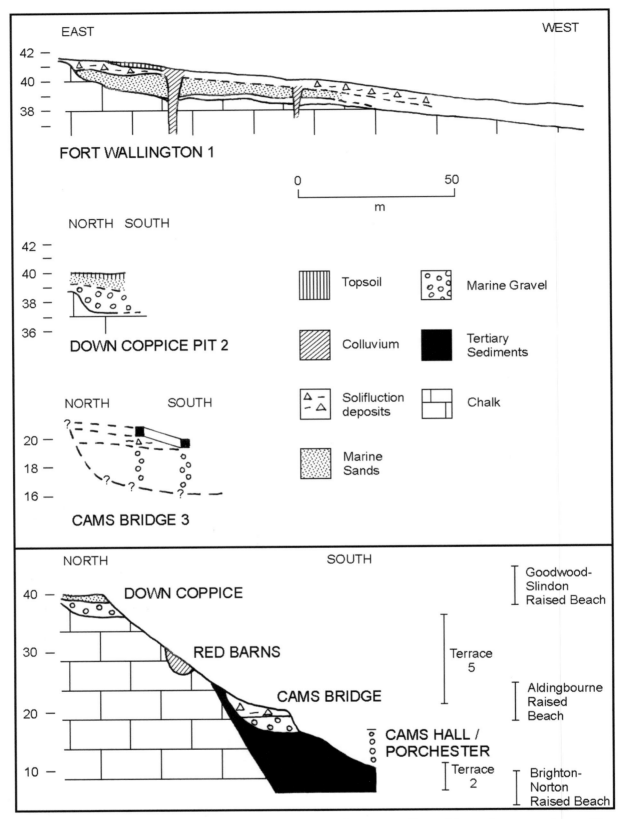

Figure 4.7: cross-profiles through key sites in the Portsdown area, Hampshire and a composite profile showing the relationship between the Down Coppice, Red Barns and Cams Bridge sites (modified from ApSimon et al. 1977)

marine origin were reported from Downend Chalk Pit (NGR SU 600065), immediately to the north of Down Coppice, and during construction of Junction 11 on the M27 motorway (ApSimon *et al.* 1977; Site 1, Figures 4.6 and 4.7). The section recorded from the M27 works indicates that stratified sands exist at the site and that the chalk bedrock rises from 36.8m to 40.1m.

Marine sediments have also been recorded from sites at lower elevations on Portsdown. A number of workers have described sediments in the vicinity of Cams Bridge (SU 601061; Site 3, Figures 4.6 and 4.7) including White (1913), Palmer & Cooke (1923, 1930) and ApSimon *et al.* (1977). These reports suggest that marine sands and gravels existed between datums of *c.*16.0m O.D. and 20m O.D. Little remains of these deposits today and major housing estates now exist within the former pit workings. A series of gravel deposits, some of which have been ascribed a marine origin, outcrop at lower elevations (10–15m O.D.) between Cams Hall and Porchester (White 1913) (Figures 4.6 and 4.7). Marine sands have also been mapped by the BGS within the Portsmouth Harbour area below datums of 10m O.D. (Figure 4.6) however, it is unclear from the mapping approach (which appears to differ between adjacent map sheets), what the criteria for mapping and age ascriptions were within the area and whether or not these sands are Pleistocene or Holocene in age.

Fluvial gravel units have also been mapped in the area. Extensive tracts of sediments mapped as Terrace 2 exist either side of Portsmouth Harbour (Figure 4.6). Fine grained silts, often mapped as 'Brickearth' appear to overlie these deposits across much of this area. Elements of older terraces have also been mapped here. It should be noted that this mapping suggests that Terrace 5 deposits appear to lie within the mouth of the Wallington at datums below those for the highest beach sequences recorded within the M27 cuttings (Figure 4.3, inset). These deposits are at higher datums than the Cams Bridge sediments within the same area. Terrace 2 deposits exist to the south at lower elevations. Elevations of the marine and fluvial deposits are shown in Figure 4.7.

This information enables the deposits to be integrated by reference to the model outlined above. It is likely that the age of the Terrace 5 deposits are younger than the raised beach sequences at elevations exceeding 30m on Portsdown. Likewise deposits of the Cams Bridge sequences are older than the Terrace 2 deposits.

THE ARUNDEL/LITTLEHAMPTON CORRIDOR

Marine deposits on the east bank of the Arun within the Arundel area, at the confluence of the Arun and the coastal plain, are dominated by an east/west

spread of beach sands and gravels south of the cliffline associated with the Brighton/Norton beach (Figure 4.8). These deposits lie below 8m O.D. and extend southwards through Angmering towards Littlehampton. To the north at higher elevations an isolated patch of marine sediments exists at datums of 8m to 12m O.D. in the vicinity of the Crossbush Bypass. At present it is difficult to relate these higher deposits to the sequences within the Chichester/Norton Farm area but one possible correlation would be with the Aldingbourne Raised Beach.

River gravels associated with the river Arun have been mapped within the valley to the west and north of Crossbush. Three terrace features have been mapped that are underlain by fluvial sediments. These have been ascribed to the 2nd, 3rd and 4th terrace of the Arun. Terrace 4 sediments exist within the area at datums intermediate between the two marine gravel deposits. Using the model outlined above it is therefore suggested that these fluvial deposits would date to the cold stage interval between the temperate phases responsible for beach formation of the two identified marine gravels. Terraces 2 and 3 are therefore likely to post-date the formation of the lower marine gravel of the Brighton–Norton beach.

DISCUSSION

The evidence described above, when used in conjunction with the model outlined previously, can be used to begin to construct frameworks for an integrated stratigraphy within the Sussex/Hampshire coastal plain area. A framework for sequence development within the coastal plain area of Sussex has previously been discussed (Bates *et al.* 1997) and four main beach sequences at differing elevations have been identified (Figure 4.2). Palaeontological evidence, coupled with independent age estimates for some units, has enabled preliminary correlations with the Marine Isotope Stratigraphy framework to be developed. Correlations of the main raised beaches of the Chichester/Arundel area with those of the Portsdown area remains problematic. However tentative correlations suggest that the Down Coppice/Fort Wallington deposits may be the equivalent of the Goodwood/Slindon raised beach. Dating and correlation of the deposits of the Solent system have previously been discussed by Allen & Gibbard (1993), Bridgland (1996) and most recently by Hosfield (1999). These studies admit major problems in attempting to formulate correlations between different parts of the Solent system. Dating of the younger elements of these sequences is constrained by a last interglacial age for the Pennington deposits (Allen *et al.* 1996) and a penultimate interglacial age for the deposits at Stone Point (Brown *et al.* 1975). Correlations between deposits on the east side of the Solent with the better

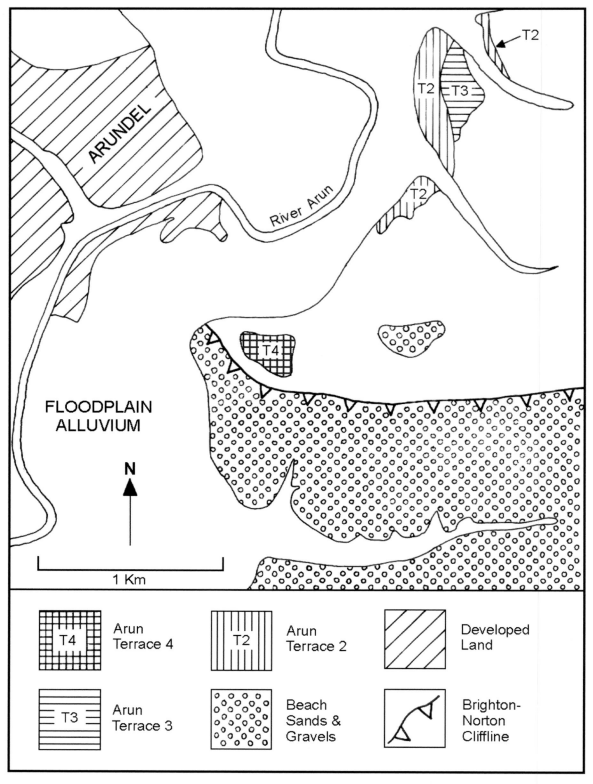

Figure 4.8: distribution of sediment units at the mouth of the river Arun (modified from British Geological Survey map 316/332, 1996)

known deposits to the west are rarely considered and no previous attempt to place the Solent system deposits into the context of the Sussex raised beaches has been made. However, using the framework provided by Allen & Gibbard (1993) and the conclusions noted in previous sections the following points can be noted:

- The Goodwood–Slindon Raised Beach can be traced westwards to Portsdown where the likely lateral correlative of this feature exists at Down Coppice Gravel Pit and in the M27 cutting.
- It is difficult to link the younger sequences of beach deposits present in the Chichester/Arundel area with those of the Portsdown area (the Cams Bridge and Cams Hall/Porchester sequences) because of height variation in the recorded sequences.
- Terrace 5 within the eastern Solent appears to exist in close proximity to the Down Coppice Gravel Pit but at lower elevations. This suggests that Terraces one to five post-date the deposition of the highest marine deposits in the area.
- Terrace 2 within the eastern Solent appears to exist at datums below the Cams Bridge marine sequences suggesting that Terraces 1 and 2 post-date the deposition of the Cams Bridge marine episode.
- Terrace 4 of the Arun lies at elevations above and to the north of the Brighton–Norton Raised Beach suggesting a minimum age for this unit during the cold stage preceding the deposition of the sediments associated with the Brighton-Norton event.

It should be noted that despite the broad correlation of raised beaches with temperate high sea levels and the major phases of river gravel aggradation with low sea levels the evidence from the Boxgrove and Norton Farm sequences indicates that individual marine sequences do not appear to represent similar parts of interglacials. The Norton Farm sequences have previously been noted to record the end of an interglacial and the transition towards colder climate conditions where cooler climates coexisted with high sea levels (Bates *et al.* 2000). Whether this is a pattern present during all interglacial/glacial transitions remains to be determined however it is interesting to note that the changes accompanying the transition from the OIS 5e to OIS 5d in the North Atlantic suggest ocean waters remained warm during initial ice build up accompanied by limited iceberg surges (Kukla 2000).

Table 4.3 attempts to provide a summary and preliminary indication of some of the possible relationships between the deposits discussed in this paper. The correlations proposed are not necessarily considered to represent a definitive statement but provide a framework model for testing and formulating future investigation strategies.

CONCLUSIONS

A model linking the patterns of changes during the temperate sea level high stand and cold, sea level low stand, events has been postulated. This model has been used to examine relationships between temperate and cold climate deposits in the vicinity of the sea level high stand estuaries/valley mouths of the Solent and Sussex river valleys.

The patterns identified and correlations postulated are however, currently only speculative and further work will be required to verify and refine these conclusions. Considerable problems in attempting to derive correlations in such situations can be noted:

- Interpretation of identified sedimentary units. Workers have often differed in their interpretation of sedimentary units on adjacent map areas resulting in a lack of continuity across map boundaries.
- Missing deposits. Even in areas recently re-mapped by the British Geological Survey key areas of Pleistocene sediments may be missing, e.g. marine sediments in the vicinity of the M27 road junction described by ApSimon *et al.* (1977) are missing from the recently published BGS map of this area (British Geological Survey 1998).
- Chronology. Even within the West Sussex Coastal Plain controversy exits regarding the age of key sites (see Roberts & Parfitt 1999). Furthermore many sites have not been dated.
- Impact of uplift. Direct correlation of sediment units across the coastal plain area may be restricted by differential uplift rates.
- Urbanism and windows of opportunity. Much of the coastal plain is heavily populated and therefore difficulties exist in gaining access to areas for investigation. However, the heavily urbanised nature of the area means that re-development and construction activity may allow opportunities for investigation in some areas.

In the future the models and correlations presented here should be tested. This may be achieved by the:

- Identification of all major geological units.
- Mapping of key identified units.
- Providing age determinations on major units.

Solent Valley (west)	Finds	Solent Valley (east)	Finds	Sussex Coastal Plain (west)	Sussex Coastal Plain (central)	Finds	Arun Valley	Adur Valley	Stage	Marine Isotope Stage (sub-Stages)
North End Copse Gravel (Buried Channel deposits)		Buried Channel deposits					Buried Channel deposits	Buried Channel deposits	Late Devensian	
										2–5b
Pennington Upper Gravel		Terrace 1					First Terrace	First Terrace	Devensian	
Pennington Marshes organic deposits					Pagham Raised Beach				Ipswichian	5e
Pennington Lower Gravel		Terrace 2					Second Terrace	Second Terrace	late Saalian	6
?Lepe Upper Gravel		Terrace 3	◆*				Third Terrace	Third Terrace		
Stone Point (Lepe) organic deposits					Brighton-Norton Raised Beach	?◆*			intra-Saalian temperate stage	7
Lepe Lower Gravel Milford-on-Sea Gravel		Terrace 4 Terrace 5	◆				Fourth Terrace Fifth Terrace			
				?Cams Hall/ Porchester Raised Beach	?Aldingbourne Raised Beach	◆				?9/11
Stanswood Bay Gravel		Terrace 6					?Sixth Terrace			
Taddiford Farm Gravel	◆*	Terrace 7								
				?Cams Bridge Raised Beach	?Aldingbourne Raised Beach	◆				?9/11
Tom's Down Gravel Old Milton Gravel	◆	Terrace 8 Terrace 9								
				?Down Coppice Raised Beach	?Goodwood–Slindon Raised Beach	◆			Pre-Anglian/ post-Cromerian (ss)	?13
Mount Pleasant Gravel		Terrace 10								
Setley Plain Gravel	◆?	Terrace 11								
				?Down Coppice Raised Beach	?Goodwood–Slindon Raised Beach					?13
Beaulieu Heath Gravel Tiptoe Gravel Sway Gravel Holmsey Ridge Gravel Whitefield Hill Gravel										

Table 4.3: lithostratigraphic correlation chart for the area of the West Sussex Coastal Plain/Hampshire Basin corridor; ◆ *Biface dominated assemblages;* * *Assemblages containing Levallois implements*

ACKNOWLEDGEMENTS

The author would like to thank Dr. Arthur ApSimon for helpful discussion during fieldwork in the Portsdown area and Dr. Phil Gibbard of the University of Cambridge for his help and constructive comments during the preparation of this paper. I would also like to thank Mr. Adrian Turgil for his help in preparing the illustrations.

REFERENCES

Allen, L.G. & Gibbard, P.L. 1993. Pleistocene evolution of the Solent River of southern England. *Quaternary Science Reviews* 12: 503–528.

Allen, L.G., Gibbard, P.L., Pettitt, M.E., Preece, R.C. & Robinson, J.E. 1996. Late Pleistocene interglacial deposits at Pennington Marshes, Lymington, Hampshire, Southern England. *Proceedings of the Geologists' Association* 107: 39–50.

ApSimon, A.M., Gamble, C.S. & Shackley, M.L. 1977. Pleistocene raised beaches on Ports Down, Hampshire. *Proceedings of the Hampshire Field Club and Archaeological Society* 33: 17–32.

Bates, M.R. 1998. Pleistocene deposits at Portfield Pit, Westhampnett East, Chichester. In J.B. Murton, C.A. Whiteman, M.R. Bates, D.R. Bridgland, A.J. Long, M.B. Roberts & M.P. Waller (ed's) *The Quaternary of Kent and Sussex: Field Guide*: 178–186. Quaternary Research Association, London.

Bates, M.R., Parfitt, S.A. & Roberts, M.B. 1997. The chronology, palaeogeography and archaeological significance of the marine Quaternary record of the West Sussex Coastal Plain, Southern England. *Quaternary Science Reviews* 16: 1227–1252.

Bates, M.R., Bates, C.R., Gibbard, P.L., Macphail, R.I., Owen, F.J., Parfitt, S.A., Preece, R.C., Roberts, M.B., Robinson, J.E., Whittaker, J.E. & Wilkinson, K.E. 2000. Late Middle Pleistocene deposits at Norton Farm on the West Sussex coastal plain, southern England. *Journal of Quaternary Science* 15: 61–89.

Bellamy, A.G. 1995. Extension of the British landmass: evidence from shelf sediment bodies in the English Channel. In R.C. Preece (ed.) *Island Britain: a Quaternary perspective*: 47–62. Geological Society Special Publication No. 96. Geological Society, London.

Berry, F.G. & Shephard-Thorn, E.R. 1982. *Geological notes and local details for 1:10000 sheets SZ 98 NW, NE, SW and SE, SZ 99 NW and NE (West Sussex Coastal Plain between Selsey and Bognor)*. Institute of Geological Sciences, Keyworth.

Bowen, D.Q. & Sykes, G. A. 1988. Correlation of marine events and glaciations on the northeast Atlantic margins. *Philosophical Transactions of the Royal Society of London Series B318*: 619–635.

Bowen, D.Q., Hughes, S., Sykes, G.A. & Miller, G.H. 1989. Land-sea correlations in the Pleistocene based on isoleucine epimerization in non-marine molluscs. *Nature* 340: 49–51.

Bridgland, D.R. 1994a. *The Quaternary of the Thames*. Chapman and Hall, London.

Bridgland, D.R. 1994b. Dating of Lower Palaeolithic industries within the framework of the Lower Thames terrace sequence. In N. Ashton & A. David (ed's) *Stories in Stone*: 28–40. Lithics Studies Society Occasional Papers 4. Lithic Studies Society, London.

Bridgland, D.R. 1996. Quaternary river terrace deposits as a framework for the Lower Palaeolithic record. In C.S. Gamble & A.J. Lawson (ed's) *The English Palaeolithic Reviewed*: 24–39. Trust for Wessex Archaeology Ltd, Salisbury.

Bristow, C.R. & Wyatt, R.J. 1983. *Geological notes and local details for 1:10000 sheets TQ 01 NW, NE, SW and SE (Pulborough and Storrington)*. Institute of Geological Sciences, Keyworth.

British Geological Survey. 1996. *Chichester and Bognor. England and Wales Sheet 317/332*. Solid and Drift Geology. 1:50,000. British Geological Survey, Keyworth.

British Geological Survey. 1998. *Fareham. England and Wales Sheet 316*. Solid and Drift Geology. 1:50,000. British Geological Survey, Keyworth.

Brown, R.C., Gilbertson, D.D., Green, C.P. & Keen, D.H. 1975. Stratigraphy and environmental significance of the Pleistocene deposits at Stone, Hampshire. *Proceedings of the Geologists' Association* 86: 349–365.

Bull, A.J. 1932. Notes on the geomorphology of the Arun Gap. *Proceedings of the Geologists' Association* 43: 274–276.

Bull, A.J. 1936. Studies in the geomorphology of the South Downs. Eastbourne to the Arun Gap. *Proceedings of the Geologists' Association* 47: 99–129.

Calkin, J.B. 1934. Implements from the higher raised beaches of Sussex. *Proceedings of the Prehistoric Society of East Anglia* 7: 333–347.

Chapman, F. 1900. The raised beach and rubble-drift at Aldrington, Between Hove and Portslade-By-Sea, Sussex. With notes on the microzoa. *Proceedings of the Geologists' Association* 16: 259–270.

Colcutt, S.N. 1999. Structural sedimentology at Boxgrove. In M.B. Roberts & S.A. Parfitt. *Boxgrove: a Middle Pleistocene hominid site at Eartham Quarry, Boxgrove, West Sussex*: 42–99. English Heritage Archaeological Report 17. English Heritage, London.

Curwen, E.C. 1925. Palaeolith from a raised beach in Sussex. *Antiquaries Journal* 5: 72–73.

Curwen, E.C. 1946. A hand-axe from the Chichester Gravels. *Proceedings of the Prehistoric Society* 12: 172–173.

Darwin-Fox, W. 1862. When and how was the Isle of Wight severed from the mainland? *The Geologist* 5: 452–454.

Dixon, F. 1850. *The geology and fossils of the Tertiary and Cretaceous formations of Sussex*. R. & J.E. Taylor, London.

Dyer, K.R. 1975. The buried channels of the 'Solent River', southern England. *Proceedings of the Geologists' Association* 86: 239–246.

Edwards, R.A. & Freshney, E.C. 1987. *Geology of the country around Southampton*. Memoir for 1:50,000 geological sheet 315 (England and Wales). HMSO, London.

Everard, C.E. 1954. The Solent River: a geomorphological study. *Transactions of the Institute of British Geographers* 20: 41–58.

Eyles, N. & MacCabe, A.M. 1991. Glaciomarine deposits of the Irish Sea Basin: the role of glacio-isostatic disequilibrium. In J. Ehlers, P.L. Gibbard & J. Rose (ed's) *Glacial deposits in Britain and Ireland*: 311–331. Balkema, Rotterdam.

Fowler, R. 1932. The "One Hundred Foot" raised beach between Arundel and Chichester, Sussex. *Quarterly Journal of the Geological Society of London* 88: 84–99.

Gamble, C.S. & ApSimon, A. 1986. 'Red Barns', Porchester. In S.N. Colcutt (ed.) *The Palaeolithic of Britain and its nearest Neighbours*: 8–12. University of Sheffield Department of Archaeology Publications, Sheffield.

Gibbard, P.L. 1988 The history of the great northwest European rivers during the past three million years. *Philosophical Transactions of the Royal Society of London Series B318*: 559–602.

Gibbard, P.L. 1995. The formation of the Strait of Dover. In R.C. Preece (ed.) *Island Britain: a Quaternary perspective*: 15–26. Geological Society Special Publication No. 96. Geological Society, London.

Gibbard, P.L. & Allen, L.G. 1994 Drainage evolution in south and east England during the Pleistocene. *Terra Nova* 6: 444–452.

Godwin-Austen, R. 1857. On the Newer Tertiary deposits of the Sussex Coast. *Quarterly Journal of the Geological Society of London* 13: 40–72.

Heron-Allen, E. 1911. *Selsey Bill: Historic and Prehistoric*. Duckworth and Co, London.

Hodgson, J.M. 1964. The low-level Pleistocene marine sands and gravels of the West Sussex Coastal Plain. *Proceedings of the Geologists' Association* 75: 547–562.

Hosfield, R. 1999. *The Palaeolithic of the Hampshire Basin. A regional model of hominid behaviour during the Middle Pleistocene*. BAR British Series 286. Archaeopress, Oxford.

Kellaway, G.A., Redding, J.K., Shephard-Thorn, E.R. & Destombes, J.P. 1975. The Quaternary history of the English Channel. *Philosophical Transactions of the Royal Society of London Series A279*: 189–218.

Kirkaldy, J.F. & Bull, A.J. 1940. The geomorphology of the rivers of the Southern Weald. *Proceedings of the Geologists' Association* 51: 115–150.

Kukla, G.J. 2000 The last interglacial. *Science* 287: 987–988.

Lautridou, J-P., Auffret, J-P., Baltzer, A., Clet, M., Lécolle, F., Lefebvre, D., Lericolais, G., Roblin-Jouve, A. Balescu, S., Carpentier, G., Descombes, J-C., Occheitti, S. & Rousseau, D-D. 1999. Le fleuve Seine, le fleuve Manche. *Bulletin de la Société de géologie de France* 170: 545–558.

Lovell, J.H. & Nancarrow, P.H.A. 1983. *The sand and gravel resources of the country around Chichester and north of Bognor Regis, Sussex. Description of 1:25,000 sheet SU 80 and 90.* Mineral Assessments Report 138. HMSO, London.

Maddy, D. 1997. Uplift driven valley-incision and river terrace formation in southern England. *Journal of Quaternary Science* 12: 539–545.

Oakley, K.P. & Curwen, E.C. 1937. The relation of the Coombe Rock to the 135ft raised beach at Slindon, Sussex. *Proceedings of the Geologists' Association* 49: 317–323.

Palmer, L.S. & Cooke, J.H. 1923. The Pleistocene deposits of the Portsmouth district and their relation to Early Man. *Proceedings of the Geologists' Association* 34: 253–282.

Palmer, L.S. & Cooke, J.H. 1930. The raised beaches near Portsmouth. *South-east Naturalist* 35: 66–75.

Preece, R.C. & Scourse, J.D. 1987. Pleistocene sea-level history in the Bembridge area of the Isle of Wight. In K.E. Barber (ed.) *Wessex and the Isle of Wight: Field Guide*: 136–149. Quaternary Research Association, Cambridge.

Preece, R.C., Scourse, J.D., Houghton, S.D., Knudsen, K.L. & Penny, D.N. 1990. The Pleistocene sea-level and neotectonic history of the eastern Solent, Southern England. *Philosophical Transactions of the Royal Society of London Series B328*: 425–477.

Prestwich, J. 1859. On the westward extension of the old raised beach of Brighton and on the extent of the sea-bed of the same period. *Quarterly Journal of the Geological Society of London* 15: 215–221.

Prestwich, J. 1872. On the presence of a raised beach on Portsdown Hill, near Portsmouth. *Quarterly Journal of the Geological Society of London* 28: 38–41.

Prestwich, J. 1892. The raised beaches and "Head" or "rubble drift" of the South of England; their relation to the valley drifts and to the Glacial Period; and on a late postglacial submergence. *Quarterly Journal of the Geological Society of London* 43: 263–343.

Reid, C. 1892. The Pleistocene deposits of the Sussex Coast and their equivalents in other districts. *Quarterly Journal of the Geological Society of London* 43: 344–361.

Reid, C. 1897. *Geology of the country around Bognor.* Memoir of the British Geological Survey, Sheet 332. HMSO, London.

Reid, C. 1902. *Geology of the country around Ringwood.* Memoir of the British Geological Survey, Sheet 314. HMSO, London.

Reid, C. 1903. *Geology of the country around Chichester.* Memoir of the British Geological Survey, Sheet 317. HMSO, London.

Reid, C. & Strahan, A. 1889, 2nd edition. *The geology of the Isle of Wight.* Memoir of the British Geological Survey.

HMSO, London.

Roberts, M.B & Parfitt, S.A. 1999. *Boxgrove: a Middle Pleistocene hominid site at Eartham Quarry, Boxgrove, West Sussex.* English Heritage Archaeological Report 17. English Heritage, London.

Shephard-Thorn, E.R. & Wymer, J.J. 1977. *Guide to X INQUA Excursion A5; South-East England and Thames Valley.* Geo Abstracts, Norwich.

Shephard-Thorn, E.R., Berry, F.G. & Wyatt, R.J. 1982. *Geological notes and local details for 1:10000 sheets SU 80 NW, NE, SW and SE, SU 90 NW, NE, SW and SE, TQ 00 NW, SW (West Sussex Coastal Plain between Chichester and Littlehampton).* Institute of Geological Sciences, Keyworth.

Stinton, F. 1985. British Quaternary fish otoliths. *Proceedings of the Geologists' Association* 96: 199–215.

Thurrell, R.G., Worssam, B.C. & Edmunds, E.A. 1968 *The Geology of the country around Haslemere.* Memoir of the British Geological Survey, Sheet 301. HMSO, London.

van Vliet-Lanoë, B., Laurent, M., Bahain, J.L., Balescu, S., Falguères, C., Field, M., Hallégouët, S. & Keen, D.H. 2000. Middle Pleistocene raised beach anomalies in the English Channel: regional and global stratigraphic implications. *Journal of Geodynamics* 29: 15–41.

Velegrakis, A.F., Dix, J.K. & Collins, M.B. 1999. Late Quaternary evolution of the upper reaches of the Solent River, Southern England, based upon marine geophysical evidence. *Journal of the Geological Society of London* 156: 73–87.

Warren, S.H. 1897. Notes on a section of the Pleistocene rubble drift near Portslade, Sussex. *Geological Magazine* 34: 302–304.

Wessex Archaeology 1994. *The Southern Rivers Palaeolithic Project. Report No. 3 1993–1994. The Sussex Raised Beaches and the Bristol Avon.* Wessex Archaeology, Salisbury.

West, I.M. 1980. Geology of the Solent estuarine system. In NERC *The Solent Estuarine System. An Assessment of the Present Knowledge*: 6–19. NERC Publication, Series C, No. 22. NERC, Swindon.

West, R.G. & Sparks, B.W. 1960. Coastal interglacial deposits of the English Channel. *Philosophical Transactions of the Royal Society of London Series B243*: 95–135.

West, R.G., Devoy, R.J.N., Funnell, B.M. & Robinson, J.E. 1984. Pleistocene deposits at Earnley, Bracklesham Bay, Sussex. *Philosophical Transactions of the Royal Society of London Series B306*: 137–157.

Whatley, R.C. & Kaye, F. 1971. The palaeoecology of Eemian (last interglacial) ostracoda from Selsey, Sussex. In H.J. Oertli (ed.) *Paléoécologie Ostracodes*: 311–330. Bulletin du Centre Recherches Pau-SPNA 5 (supp.)

White, H.J.O. 1913. *The geology of the country near Fareham and Havant.* Memoir of the British Geological Survey, Sheet 316. HMSO, London.

White, H.J.O. 1924. *Geology of the country around Brighton and Worthing.* Memoir of the British Geological Survey, Sheets 318 and 333. HMSO, London.

Woodcock, A. 1981. *The Lower and Middle Palaeolithic periods in Sussex.* British Archaeological Reports British Series 94. BAR, Oxford.

Wymer, J.J. 1988. Palaeolithic archaeology and the British

Quaternary Sequence. *Quaternary Science Reviews* 7: 79–98.

Young, B. & Lake, R.D. 1988. *Geology of the Country around Brighton and Worthing*. Memoir of the British Geological Survey, Sheets 318 and 333. HMSO, London.

5. SOME EARLIER PALAEOLITHIC FIND-SPOTS OF INTEREST IN THE SOLENT REGION

D.A. Roe

ABSTRACT

Over 30 years ago, the author listed many Lower Palaeolithic find-spots in the area of the Solent gravels and the lower reaches of the river valleys which drain to the Solent, on the basis of artefacts surviving in museum collections and/or recorded in the literature up to about 1965. Amongst the large quantity of material he encountered, there was some that at the time seemed of more than average interest. Even though many of the finds were made a very long while ago, their potential significance may actually have tended to increase rather than diminish, in the light of all the changes to our knowledge of the British Pleistocene and Palaeolithic that have taken place since then. If there is to be a new surge of interest in the Pleistocene deposits of the Solent region, it seems desirable that these old finds should not be forgotten, in case opportunities occur to re-examine any of the find-spots and gain proper information about them. The recent work of John Wymer for the Southern Rivers and English Rivers projects has already greatly helped this cause, but it remains true that relatively few people have returned to the old artefact collections themselves.

INTRODUCTION

This paper is based on a fifteen-minute presentation, for which I did not write a formal text. The talk was illustrated with 17 slides, which I cannot of course reproduce here, although suitable illustrations have been included where possible. No tight definition of what constituted the extent of the Solent River was given to speakers, and indeed we were encouraged to range as widely as we saw fit. I had also arranged in advance with the organisers of the meeting that Mr Brian Hack should display a substantial selection of the artefacts which he (like the late Chris Draper before him) had patiently and carefully collected from Rainbow Bar, a very interesting gravel feature exposed at low tide off Fareham. I referred in my own talk to Rainbow Bar, and allowed Mr Hack's exhibition and accompanying documentation to serve as illustration. As regards the paper I gave, I will adopt here the format of reporting what I said, with relevant references added, and indicating what I had in mind in selecting the various points and topics, hoping that the result may prove readable and informative. The meeting was a pleasant and informal occasion, with a well-chosen group of invited participants, who learned a lot from each other. Perhaps this volume will enable others who could not be there to share the spirit of the occasion as well as the knowledge that emerged from it.

My original title referred to 'Lower Palaeolithic' find-spots: I have altered this to the more general 'Earlier Palaeolithic', in view of the fact that I included some sites that had yielded handaxes of *bout-coupé* type — generally accepted as being of Mousterian origin and therefore Middle Palaeolithic for those who use that term.

APPROACHING THE ARCHAEOLOGICAL EVIDENCE FROM THE SOLENT AREA

It being still early in January when the meeting took place, I began by saying that I would greet the year 2000 by delivering the most backward-looking and out-of-date paper that anyone would be likely to hear during it. I hope this statement was actually erroneous, but I explained that I had collected much of the data about which I would be speaking during the early 1960s and (as I had expected might be the case) there were clearly some members of the audience who had not yet been born when I was doing that, as a graduate research student at Cambridge. Little had changed, however, in the basic primary classification of the gathered information, and one would also have to admit that very few of the problems concerning the dating and nature of the principal Palaeolithic occurrences in Hampshire and adjoining counties had been solved in the interim. Indeed, few of them had even been addressed, which made the calling of this meeting a very encouraging sign. On the credit side, the range of possible answers to the basic questions had vastly increased, and there had been some spectacular discoveries of sites not too far from Southampton, which had profoundly affected our whole perception of the British Earlier Palaeolithic — most notably Boxgrove (Roberts & Parfitt 1999) but also Red Barns (Gamble & ApSimon 1986; Wenban-Smith *et al.* 2000).

Perhaps the most influential change since the 1960s, however, was our much better understanding of the length and complexity of the British Pleistocene sequence, and the general move towards use of Oxygen Isotope Stages to indicate the age of important local deposits. The dating of British Palaeolithic sites was no longer unrealistically contracted to fit a system with just three glacial and four interglacial events, and the chances of understanding the relationships of the local sites to each other, and of establishing correlations with other regional sequences, were correspondingly much better. As for what constituted the Solent region, I suggested that to understand it one needed to consider not only the Pleistocene deposits on the mainland and the Isle of Wight that might actually relate to the main course of the Pleistocene 'Solent River', but also those in the valleys of the tributary rivers, in Hampshire, Wiltshire and Dorset, perhaps in some cases right back to their sources.

My own study of Solent Region artefacts in museum and private collections had been part of a general survey, eventually published as the C.B.A's *Gazetteer of British Lower and Middle Palaeolithic Sites* (Roe 1968). It was a pleasure to turn next to the work of John Wymer, who had recently completed his long Southern and English Rivers survey projects, which had resulted in the publication not only of the important regional survey volumes but also of his book *The Lower Palaeolithic Occupation of Britain* (Wymer 1999). Reviewing some years ago Wymer's volume on the East Anglian Palaeolithic (Wymer 1985), I had said that, now he had dealt so effectively with the Thames Valley (Wymer 1968) and East Anglia, it would be wonderful (though hardly fair to expect it) if he ever turned his attention to the third great area of concentrated Lower Palaeolithic settlement in Britain, central southern England and the Solent region in particular. In the recent publications, he had now done much more than that, and it was good to see that the Solent region had received full and generous coverage. It had certainly been a major area of settlement in Britain right through the Earlier Palaeolithic, and it was curious that there was much less completed research relating to it than to the Lower and Middle Thames or to East Anglia.

Yet even Wymer in his latest book (Wymer 1999) had only been able to divide the British Earlier Palaeolithic material into three broad periods: Period I, for everything up to the end of Oxygen Isotope Stage 12 (the Anglian cold stage); Period II from the start of Stage 11 to the end of Stage 8; and Period III for sites younger than Stage 8, which he classed as Middle Palaeolithic. Where no geological dating evidence was available for an assemblage of artefacts, his strategy had been to look for such diagnostic features as Levalloisian technology or *bout-coupé* handaxes, but there were still many large accumulations of probably mixed artefacts from individual gravel pits or other find-spots of which even he could make little.

Following up my threat to adopt a thoroughly out-of-date approach, and after a cautious glance round to see who was present, I said that I proposed to ask whether there might be anything at all in the old ideas about artefact typology and technology — particularly for handaxes — that might actually offer us any useful guidance, even within the broadest limits. Before the entire audience could flee the room in horror, I added that if we did indeed find that any of the Solent area assemblages bore a strong resemblance in such terms to others from elsewhere in Britain, the whole question of how such resemblances were to be interpreted was now far more complex and relevant than a bland assumption that precise contemporaneity or a close cultural connection must be the answer. Instead, the explanation of morphological similarity might be that it was constrained or controlled by use of some particular kind of raw material, or was reflecting similarity in function, or implied some specific human ecological adaptation. These things were all major topics, but in this brief presentation I could do no more than suggest that in the British Earlier Palaeolithic there were indeed a number of sets of assemblages that did seem to resemble each other quite strikingly, whatever might be the explanation, and I would select just four examples to illustrate this. In each case, I believed that there were local representatives of that group to be found in the Solent region. Some of the relevant site names were largely forgotten and deserved to be better known, especially if opportunities might arise at some time in the future to examine and sample relevant exposures at any of those places.

SOME SOLENT SITES IN THEIR BRITISH CONTEXT

Clactonian

I began by showing a slide of British Clactonian artefacts, there being various well-known Clactonian sites in Britain, some of which had been the subject of recent field-work or other study. Apart from the occurrences at Clacton itself, the leading sites included the Lower Gravels at Barnfield and Rickson's Pits at Swanscombe (Kent), Barnham (Suffolk), the Highlands Farm Pit near Henley (Oxfordshire), and a number of pits in the Thurrock area (Essex). This was not an occasion to discuss the fascinating and important problems relating to the nature or significance of the Clactonian in Britain, but simply to note it as a limited but consistent phenomenon in the British Middle Pleistocene, apparently present before the beginning of Oxygen Isotope Stage 11, and perhaps lasting until Stage 9. It was essentially of 'Mode 1' character, i.e. it contained cores and flakes worked by 'hard-hammer' flaking, with a limited range of retouched tool types, but little or no sign of regular handaxe manufacture.

Since typical products of hard-hammer flaking could be found in many Palaeolithic industries, it would not be appropriate to use the term 'Clactonian' unless one were dealing with a substantial assemblage wholly of Mode 1 character and arguably of Middle Pleistocene age. In the Solent area there was one very interesting site which might or might not prove to meet these criteria: Rainbow Bar. Artefacts had been collected here in great numbers from a gravel exposed on the foreshore only during periods of very low tide (Draper 1951; Hack 1999). Many were cores and flakes of Mode 1 appearance, though some had been described as bifaces or proto-bifaces, and there was also a little material likely to be of Holocene age. One might recall the situation at Lion Point, Clacton, where genuine Clactonian artefacts were collected from a gravel that was exposed only at low tide, but some later prehistoric material could certainly be found lying on the surface amongst them. In the case of Rainbow Bar, it seemed that the cobbles forming the gravel were also the source of raw material for the artefacts themselves, and it might be that they were exploited during a number of different periods before the feature was eventually covered by the present sea. At present, the age of the Rainbow Bar gravel was completely unknown, and the possibility that some of the material associated with it was actually Clactonian, as opposed to being an industry of younger age but archaic technological appearance, remained a matter of mere typological opinion, which could solve nothing. It was not easy to see from the location of the gravel that it was likely to be of early date, but some kind of coordinated geological and archaeological operation during the times of best exposure might be able to provide answers to at least some of the questions it raised. Large numbers of collected artefacts were available for study, including those in Mr Hack's collection. Whether the gravel might contain any faunal material or other environmental evidence was at present unknown. My own view was that Rainbow Bar was a site well worth further investigation, and I particularly wished to bring it to the attention of this meeting's audience; Mr Hack would certainly welcome active interest from Quaternary researchers.

Acheulian

I next showed a slide of handaxes from Corfe Mullen, Dorset, certainly a Solent region site on any definition (Figure 5.1). These were a combination of flat, refined, rather square-ended ovates and crudely made, thick, pointed or pear-shaped handaxes, apparently shaped by hard-hammer flaking. The Corfe Mullen artefacts and the local gravel deposits had been studied half a century ago by Calkin & Green (1949; see also Roe 1975 & 1981: 189–91), and it was mainly the geology that had received more recent attention. Wymer in his recent book (1999: 106, 110) had allowed for the possibility that at least some of the artefacts were *in situ* in gravels of Terrace 12 of the proto-Solent, and that their age would therefore fall within his Period 1, but had stopped short of drawing this as a firm conclusion.

Using the typological and technological evidence precisely as threatened, I said that I would certainly expect that dating to prove correct, if the deposits could be restudied. The combination of the handaxe types seemed to me to be exactly what could be seen in gravels elsewhere in southern England that are known to be of Anglian or pre-Anglian age, notably at Warren Hill in Suffolk (Figure 5.2) and at Highlands Farm Pit in Oxfordshire. I illustrated the same combination of fine ovates and crude hard-hammer handaxes from these sites, and pointed out that the ovates there were like those of Corfe Mullen not just at a general but also at a detailed level, with their square-ended plan-forms, frequency of tranchet finish blows, and absence of twisted profiles. The Warren Hill gravels had been clearly shown to be part of a pre-Anglian drainage system in East Anglia, the Bytham Sands and Gravels (see for example Rose *et al.* 1996), and the so called Ancient Channel Gravels in which the Highlands Farm site occurs were of Black Park Terrace age in the Thames Valley (Bridgland 1994: 141–5). In the case of Highlands Farm, Clactonian artefacts were also present in large numbers, as well as the two kinds of handaxes.

Given the generally consistent different physical condition of the different artefact types, it seemed likely, though not provable, that at Warren Hill and Highlands Farm we were seeing separate human

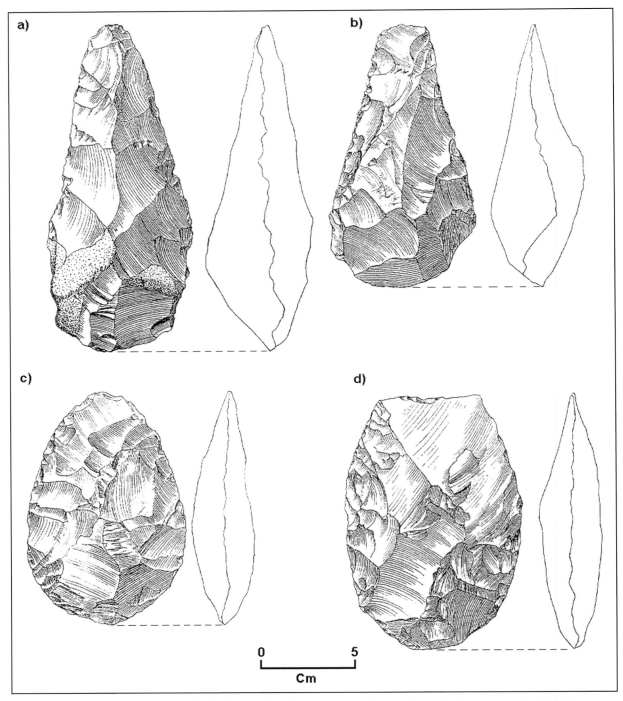

Figure 5.1: handaxes from Corfe Mullen: a–b) thick, pointed "pear-shaped" forms from Ballast Hole; c–d) finely made ovates with tranchet sharpening from Cogdean Pit, d) with square-ended planform (Calkin & Green 1949)

industries which had been brought together and mixed at the time of formation of the deposits that now contained them. In any case, such industries could be seen unmixed elsewhere — for example, the crude handaxes at Kent's Cavern, Devonshire, and the fine ovates of that particular type at Boxgrove. My suggestion accordingly was that Corfe Mullen offered a Solent region parallel to the Warren Hill situation. I repeated that there was at present no unequivocal

dating evidence to support this assertion; the key matters to be resolved by any possible future work would be the age of the gravel on the one hand, and the relationship of the artefacts to it on the other. Meanwhile, it seemed to me entirely justifiable to state the typological and technological situation, stressing its shortcomings, and see whether the challenge could eventually be taken up. Since several well-dated Lower Palaeolithic sites of Stage 13 or 12

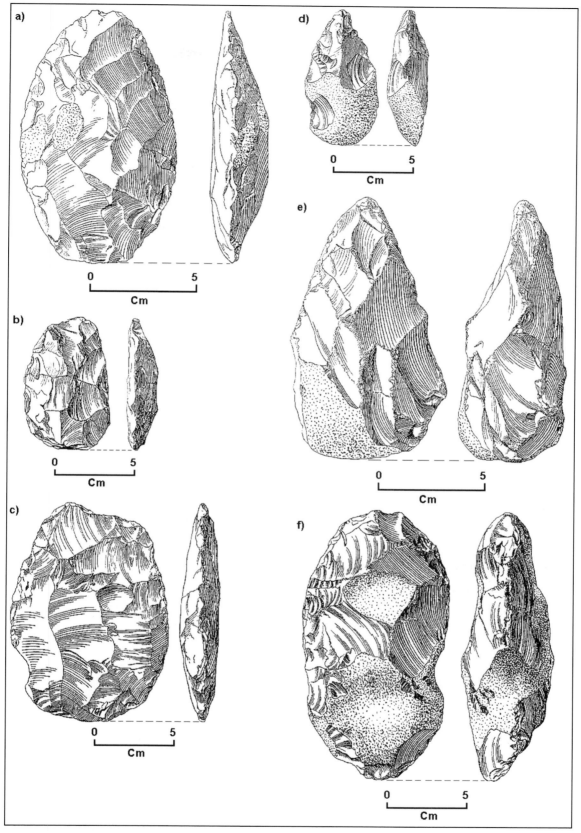

Figure 5.2: handaxes from Warren Hill: a–c) well-made ovates in fresh condition with soft-hammer flaking and blunt or square-ended planforms; d–f) crude implements made wholly by hard-hammer flaking (Smith 1931)

age were now known in different parts of Britain, it would be rather surprising if the Solent region had not been visited at this time.

I next suggested that there was a particular version of the Acheulian in Britain which had not perhaps received the attention it deserved, though there were many sites attributable to it. The starting point was again a typological one, in line with my theme. Such industries, often prolific, featured large pointed handaxes (including the classic ficron type), heavy rather narrow ovates, (often with a squared tip), and — as perhaps the most striking element — large cleavers, with wide axe-like edges at the tip end. A difficulty was to find examples of this Acheulian facies other than in a secondary context. Two of the best occurrences were the sites of Furze Platt and Baker's Farm in the Middle Thames Valley (summarised in Roe 1981: 164–8, though the geological arguments are out-of-date), but in both cases the artefacts had been somewhat disturbed. A far better site was Cuxton, in Kent (Tester 1965; Cruse 1988).

I could not on this occasion discuss the age of these sites, which were probably younger than the Swanscombe Middle Gravels Acheulian, or consider whether the character of the large tools might relate to specific human activities, but it seemed to me that there were several examples of this kind of Acheulian in the Solent region: I showed slides of the typical handaxe and cleaver forms from the Test Road Materials Pit near Romsey (Figure 5.3), and also from Warsash. In the latter case, only sporadic attention had been given to the implements since the account published over 60 years ago by Burkitt, Paterson & Mogridge (1939). This was a case where only careful inspection of the old collections could have revealed that this Acheulian variant was well represented in the Solent region. The classic cleavers, accompanied by the other types mentioned, come from several find-spots in the Bournemouth area, notably Winton, and in the Southampton area, notably Old Shirley. I also particularly mentioned the Highfield Church brickfield, not knowing that Francis Wenban-Smith would devote particular attention to it in a later paper (see Chapter 6). Those working locally on the Solent region Palaeolithic should keep watch for new exposures in which artefacts of this particular type occurred, perhaps in a context that could be closely dated, or in a condition that might allow a study of their particular functions.

I concluded my survey of the Lower Palaeolithic by reporting that in the Solent region one further important variant of the British Acheulian, this time quite scarce, was represented, though again one needed to go to the old collections to discover this. The variant in question had been referred to as 'Late Acheulian or Micoquian', and the best site was certainly still the Wolvercote Channel, Oxford (see for example Roe 1981: 118–128; Tyldesley 1986),

Figure 5.3: handaxes from Test Road Materials Pit, Romsey in teaching collections at Donald Baden-Powell Quaternary Research Centre, University of Oxford (photo V.P. Narracott), including a ficron (lower row, left) and a cleaver (lower row, centre)

even though it had so far proved impossible to relocate it for more up-to-date examination. Traditionally this variant, characterised by fine pointed handaxes made by a highly distinctive plano-convex technique (Figures 5.4–5.5), had been regarded as of Upper Pleistocene 'Last Interglacial' age, at the very end of the Acheulian tradition, but our better understanding of the Pleistocene succession might well cause an earlier age to be assigned to it; its relationship to the Continental European Micoquian remained a matter of great interest. Without having time to explore these matters, I pointed out that isolated examples of the typical plano-convex handaxes existed from several sites in the Southampton area and the Test Valley, but that more substantial quantities of them appeared to have come from Warsash (cf. Burkitt *et al.* 1939: 40 and Figs. 7–8), and from Shirley Church (e.g. material at Winchester Museum), though in both cases mixed assemblages were present. Wenban-Smith *et al.*'s recent analysis (2000) of the assemblage from Red Barns has also emphasised the predominance at that

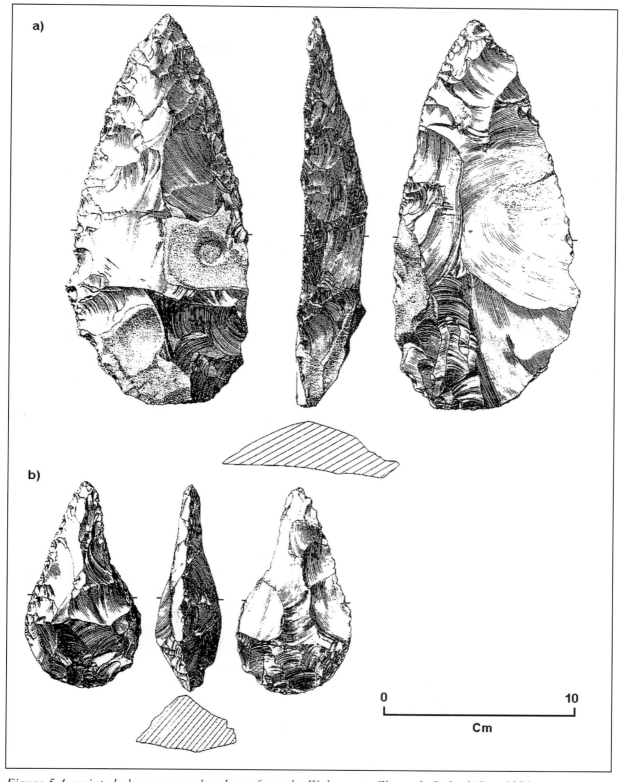

Figure 5.4: pointed plano-convex handaxes from the Wolvercote Channel, Oxford (Roe 1981)

site of often finely worked plano-convex handaxes. This handaxe type would again be worth watching for in any new local exposures of Late Middle Pleistocene or Early Upper Pleistocene age.

Middle Palaeolithic

I did not follow Wymer's suggestion, previously referred to, that anything of younger age than Oxygen Isotope Stage 8 should be classed as Middle Palaeolithic, nor did I comment on the occurrence of

53

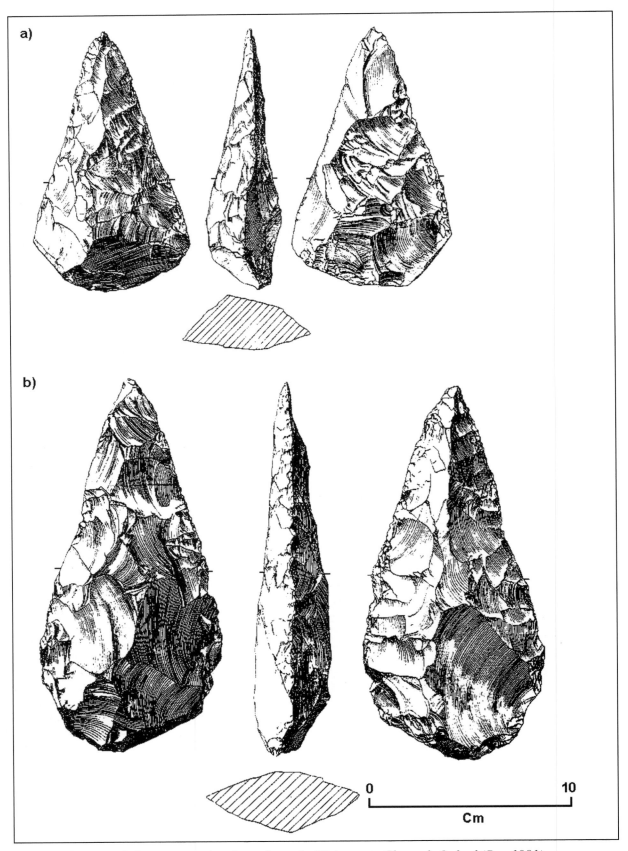

Figure 5.5: pointed plano-convex handaxes from the Wolvercote Channel, Oxford (Roe 1981)

Levalloisian technique within the Solent region, but I did refer to the presence of several examples of the important *bout-coupé* handaxe type, widely regarded as representing the only segment of the whole 'Mousterian' complex that ever reached Britain — the Mousterian of Acheulian Tradition. Occurrences of these distinctive handaxes were rarely found in datable contexts, but when they were they seemed attributable to milder phases of the Last Glaciation. I had summarised the British distribution of *bout-coupé* handaxes, sometimes alternatively referred to as 'flat-butted cordates', nearly 20 years ago (Roe 1981: 250–67), and they had subsequently been given much fuller treatment by J. Tyldesley (1987). I agreed entirely with Wymer's latest (1999) comments about them, but in those he had mainly been agreeing with myself and Joyce Tyldesley anyhow. A full list of the Solent area finds could be gleaned from these various sources. As examples, I showed the two particularly fine and often illustrated examples from Bournemouth (Southbourne Broadway and Castle Lane, Moordown; see Calkin and Green 1949: 31–5); the specimen from brickearth at Fisherton, near Salisbury, found as long ago as 1864 and illustrated by Sir John Evans in the first edition of his *Ancient Stone Implements* (1872: 551); and a slide given to me long ago by the late Chris Draper of two damaged examples found together in the garden of 40, Blackbrook Park Avenue, Fareham. Elsewhere in the region, Great Pan Farm, Shide, on the Isle of Wight (Poole 1925; Shackley 1973), was an important site, in which a *bout-coupé* handaxe apparently formed part of a substantial Mousterian of Acheulian Tradition assemblage, with other handaxes, cores, flake tools and flakes. One could conclude that the British Mousterian, such as it was, was well represented in the Solent region.

To conclude my review on a slightly different note, and to make a not solely ritual escape from the shackles of typology, I ended by drawing to the audience's attention a much overlooked paper on the local Lower Palaeolithic by, of all people, the late Professor Christopher Hawkes, better known as a towering figure in the archaeology of much later periods (Hawkes 1943). While working at the British Museum in 1939, he had been assigned the task of reporting on two handaxes from the immensely prolific site of Broom, on the Dorset–Devon border, famous since the 19th century for its handaxes of Greensand chert. One of the two had been made of flint, however, and in the course of a typically scholarly paper Hawkes pointed to the occurrence of a proportion of handaxes in the Broom collections which appeared to be made of grey Hampshire flint, and the corresponding presence of Lower Palaeolithic artefacts made of Greensand chert at some of the leading Hampshire sites. He suggested that this might be indicating movement of people between the two areas at various times during the Lower Palaeolithic.

Hawkes was basing his comments simply on the collections (admittedly large) available to him at the British Museum; in my general survey of the main collections all over Britain during the early 1960s, I had been able to note many other examples of flint implements at Broom and chert implements at Hampshire and Dorset sites. Being aware that Dr G. Marshall would be discussing the finds from Broom later in the day (see Chapter 8), I did not myself go into further details, but just used the facts to stress again the usefulness of consulting the older literature and the old artefact collections: Hawkes' observation seemed to me a very perceptive one, especially for the date when it was made, and I wondered whether he might not have been right, in general terms, in his interpretation. We would see what Dr Marshall thought.

CONCLUSION

This was a brief, general review, serious in intention but not too weighty in presentation, and I hope some of the points in this account of it will be of interest to those who were not at the meeting. The message from it is that the Solent region is of great importance to the British Earlier Palaeolithic, and that there is every reason to suppose that all the major stages of the latter will have been represented there. The whole question of the Solent River and its Pleistocene history is of real significance to Quaternary Research in Britain, and Palaeolithic archaeologists should take the opportunity of the current interest in it, to which other papers in this volume refer, to enhance in any way they can our knowledge and understanding of the early human settlement of the region, whether it be by solving problems of chronology, by gaining new information about the successive environments in which the people lived, by locating new Palaeolithic sites or rediscovering old ones, or in any other way. If the meeting in January 2000 has helped to focus local interest on the research potential of the Solent region, and to forge alliances of Quaternary researchers ready to tackle specific problems as opportunities arise, then the day was well spent indeed. Meanwhile, constant local vigilance is desirable: it would be sad if even brief exposures of potentially important Pleistocene sediments were to come and go without examination, anywhere in the network of valleys that once made up the drainage basin of the Solent River.

REFERENCES

Bridgland, D.R. 1994. *Quaternary of the Thames*. Chapman and Hall, London.

Burkitt, M.C., Paterson, T.T. & Mogridge, C.J. 1939. The Lower Palaeolithic industries near Warsash, Hampshire.

Proceedings of the Prehistoric Society 5: 39–50.

Calkin, J.B. & Green, J.F.N. 1949. Palaeoliths and terraces near Bournemouth. *Proceedings of the Prehistoric Society* 15: 21–37.

Cruse, R.J. 1988. Further investigation of the Acheulian site at Cuxton. *Archaeologia Cantiana* 104: 39–81.

Draper, C.J. 1951. Stone industries from Rainbow Bar, Hants. *Archaeological Newsletter* 3(9): 147–9.

Evans, (Sir) J. 1872, 1st edition. *The Ancient Stone Implements, Weapons, and Ornaments, of Great Britain.* Longmans, Green, Reader & Dyer, London.

Gamble, C.S. & A.M. ApSimon. 1986. Red Barns — Portchester. In S.N. Collcutt (ed.) *The Palaeolithic of Britain and its Nearest Neighbours. Recent Trends*: 8–12. Department of Archaeology and Prehistory, University of Sheffield.

Hack, B. 1999. More stone tools from Rainbow Bar. *Proceedings of the Hampshire Field Club and Archaeological Society* 54: 163–71.

Hawkes, C.F.C. 1943. Two Palaeoliths from Broom, Dorset. *Proceedings of the Prehistoric Society* 9: 48–52.

Poole, H.F. 1925. Palaeoliths from Great Pan Farm, Isle of Wight. *Papers and Proceedings of the Hampshire Field Club* 9: 305–19.

Roberts, M.B. & Parfitt, S.A. 1999. *Boxgrove: a Middle Pleistocene Hominid Site at Eartham Quarry, Boxgrove, West Sussex.* English Heritage, London.

Roe, D.A. 1968. *A Gazetteer of British Lower and Middle Palaeolithic Sites* (Research Report No 8). Council for British Archaeology, London.

Roe, D.A. 1975. Some Hampshire and Dorset handaxes and the question of 'Early Acheulian' in Britain. *Proceedings of the Prehistoric Society* 41: 1–9.

Roe, D.A. 1981. *The Lower and Middle Palaeolithic Periods in Britain.* Routledge & Kegan Paul, London.

Rose, J., Allen, P., Green, C.P., Hey, R.W., Lewis, S.G., Sinclair, J.M. & Whiteman, C.A. 1996. The Kesgrave and Bytham Sands and Gravels of East Anglia. *Newsletter of the Quaternary Research Association* 79: 10–25.

Shackley, M.L. 1973. A contextual study of the Mousterian industry from Great Pan Farm, Isle of Wight. *Proceedings of the Isle of Wight Natural History and Archaeological Society* 6: 542–54.

Smith, R.A. 1931. *The Sturge collection: an illustrated selection of flints from Britain bequeathed in 1919 by William Allen Sturge MVO, MD, FCRP.* British Museum, London.

Tester, P.J. 1965. An Acheulian site at Cuxton. *Archaeologia Cantiana* 80: 30–60.

Tyldesley, J.A. 1986. *The Wolvercote Channel Handaxe Assemblage. A Comparative Study.* BAR British Series 153. British Archaeological Reports, Oxford.

Tyldesley, J.A. 1987. *The Bout Coupé Handaxe: a Typological Problem.* BAR British Series 170. British Archaeological Reports, Oxford.

Wenban-Smith, F.F., Gamble, C.S. & ApSimon, A.M. 2000. The Lower Palaeolithic site at Red Barns, Portchester, Hampshire: bifacial technology, raw material quality and the organisation of archaic behaviour. *Proceedings of the Prehistoric Society* 66: 209–255.

Wymer, J.J. 1968. *Lower Palaeolithic Archaeology in Britain, as represented by the Thames Valley.* John Baker, London.

Wymer, J.J. 1985. *Palaeolithic Sites of East Anglia.* Geo Books, Norwich.

Wymer, J.J. 1999. *The Lower Palaeolithic Occupation of Britain.* Wessex Archaeology and English Heritage, Salisbury.

6. AS REPRESENTED BY THE SOLENT RIVER: HANDAXES FROM HIGHFIELD, SOUTHAMPTON

F.F. Wenban-Smith

ABSTRACT

Wymer suggested in 1968 that the archaeological sequence from successive terraces in a major Pleistocene drainage basin such as the Thames could serve as a model for the British Lower and Middle Palaeolithic as a whole. Although sites such as Hoxne, High Lodge and Boxgrove have now demonstrated this is not the case, no comparable study of archaeological change within the sequence of a different drainage basin has taken place. If certain premises concerning the relation of lithic typology/technology to Palaeolithic behaviour are accepted, then the potential exists ultimately for the investigation of issues such as range and mobility, as well as date. Study of material from Highfield in Southampton has revealed both internal diversity at one location within a single terrace unit, and distinctive features absent in the Thames sequence. This demonstrates the regional nature of the gross Palaeolithic cultural record, and highlights the necessity for the construction of frameworks of cultural change beyond, and at a finer spatial resolution than, the Thames Valley. It also emphasises the importance of improving understanding of the chronological and spatial resolution of artefact collections from river terrace deposits if their interpretive potential is to be expanded.

INTRODUCTION

The small case study presented here arose out of a re-examination of the material from Red Barns, Portchester (Wenban-Smith *et al.* 2000). The lithic technology at the site was dominated by the production of pointed plano-convex handaxes. The dating evidence, however, was limited, being restricted to "some time post-Boxgrove, *c.* 500,000–5,000 BP" on lithostratigraphic grounds, and "some time in the range Oxygen Isotope Stage 11 to 7, *c.* 425,000–200,000 BP" on biostratigraphic (a horse bone) and chronometric (amino acid epimerization) grounds. In view of the distinctive plano-convex handaxe technology, it seemed worth considering whether this could contribute to dating the site more accurately within this range.

The use of certain tool types as type-fossils to characterise the age or cultural affinity of assemblages has had a bad press over the last 50 years. Bradley & Sampson (1986), for instance, have suggested that the use of typology for dating purposes is now wholly superseded by harder Quaternary sciences and their "battery of dating techniques" (*ibid.* 29). If only this was always so, but sadly, and especially in the Solent region, this vaunted battery has often failed to produce results. Whether or not handaxe typology, or lithic technology generally, is even potentially useful for dating depends upon a range of premises concerning the production of lithic artefacts. Before the 1960s, these were generally regarded as so self-evident that they were left implicit. Then L. and S. Binford (1966 & 1969), in particular, challenged these assumptions, partly by merely pointing out their presence. At the same time they provided an alternative functional paradigm to explain broadly synchronic lithic variability within a region. Following this theoretical assault, improved dating of several Lower Palaeolithic assemblages from Britain — Hoxne (Wymer 1974 & 1983), High Lodge (Ashton *et al.* 1992) and Boxgrove (Roberts *et al.* 1994; Roberts & Parfitt 1999) —

confirmed that existing models, such as Wymer's (1968), for the nature and trajectory of cultural change within the British Lower Palaeolithic needed to be rethought. Despite these challenges, the notion of periods within the British Lower/Middle Palaeolithic characterised by distinctive lithic technology or tool-types has proved remarkably resilient. Shackley (1977), Tyldesley (1986 & 1987) and White (1998a) continued to relate certain specific types of handaxe to populations with specific cultural traditions (in the sense of a repertoire of technological practices/habits acquired, developed and transmitted within the context of a community) operating in particular regions at particular periods. And many workers, including this writer, continue to regard the distinctive assemblages labelled as Clactonian (Wenban-Smith 1998; White 2000) and Levalloisian (Bridgland 1996) as representing the product of particular cultural traditions in the same way.

The first part of this paper reviews some premises and behavioural models on which the use of lithic typology and technology in dating must be predicated. If certain premises are provisionally accepted, there is a case for attempting the construction of regional frameworks of technological and typological change, based on broad relatively datable litho-stratigraphic units such as fluvial terrace formations. This can provide a framework for both the dating of material from less securely dated geological contexts, and potentially also the basis for the investigation of the range and mobility of Lower/Middle Palaeolithic populations.

The remainder of the paper focuses on a case study of handaxes from a single site in the Highfield area of Southampton. The starting point of this investigation was the idea that handaxe typology *might* potentially be applicable in dating Red Barns more accurately. Consequently a sample of material from different Solent River terraces in Southampton was examined. This small-scale preliminary study did not, however, reveal any plano-convex handaxes so this approach to dating Red Barns was abandoned. The samples of material studied from the different terraces were, however, remarkable for the diversity of handaxe types and the recurring presence of typological and technological oddities unfamiliar to the writer, more familiar with material from East Anglia and the Lower Thames. Consequently a follow-up study was conducted, in which all the material from one locality in one terrace was examined.

LITHICS AND DATING

Early in the history of Palaeolithic archaeology, several initial assumptions concerning the lithic material culture that constitutes its main evidence in the present day were taken entirely for granted. Central amongst these was the notion of a "culture" in which a community linked by a shared social milieu produced distinctive types or assemblages of lithic artefacts following the cultural tradition of the community. Subsidiary assumptions included the notion of continual (although slow) cultural progress, and the projection of a subjective aesthetic of quality and refinement onto the lithic artefacts. Together with the broad chronological framework provided by geological context, these principles provided the basis for the initial organisation of the Palaeolithic archaeological record into the classic pan (northwest) European framework of Lower, Middle and Upper Palaeolithic, and for identifying stages within this broad framework, on the basis of *instruments caractèristiques*, or type fossils (de Mortillet G. & A. 1900; Breuil & Koslowski 1931 & 1932).

Although the overall tripartite division of the Palaeolithic into Lower, Middle and Upper has proved reasonably robust, more detailed subdivision of the Lower and Middle Palaeolithic into stages based on material culture has proved elusive, continually undermined by i) improving understanding of the Pleistocene chrono-stratigraphic framework and the place within it of certain lithic assemblages, and ii) changing perspectives on the relationship between human behaviour and material cultural variability. In Britain, Wymer's (1968) model for the Lower/Middle Palaeolithic sequence, based on material from the terrace sequence of the Thames Valley, has been contradicted by the assemblages from sites such as High Lodge (Ashton *et al.* 1992), Hoxne (Wymer 1974 & 1983) and Boxgrove (Roberts *et al.* 1994; Roberts & Parfitt 1999). And on the theoretical side, workers such as Binford (1983) have argued that tool-making, using and discard behaviour is liable to be patchily distributed around a landscape, corresponding to the distribution of different resources and activities, leading to the possibility that the same human group could leave typologically and/or technologically different archaeological signatures at different locations across its range. Several workers have also argued, albeit questionably (cf. Wenban-Smith 2000a), that the typological and technological variations of the Lower/Middle Palaeolithic record are not in fact deliberately imposed shape or technical preferences, but merely the unintended products of varying intensities of re-sharpening (Dibble 1987), the application of a generalised bifacial knapping approach to raw material of varying shape and quality (Ashton & McNabb 1994; White 1998b), or the result of investment in technology as part of a role in sexual selection (Kohn & Mithen 1999).

The recognition that Palaeolithic technology and typology a) did not change through time in Britain as once expected and in accordance with Wymer's (1968) model, and b) was potentially subject to a range of functional, social and situational influences, does not, however, necessarily mean that useful chronological indicators are absent from the Lower and Middle Palaeolithic archaeological record; nor that human groups have not carried out distinctive cultural practices whose products can provide useful indicators of their presence in particular regions during certain time periods. After all, the finding of a coke can on the moon would reasonably lead to a presumption of a post-19th century human visit. What is necessary is to support any proposed frameworks as far as possible by independent dating evidence, and to work with rather than against the characteristics of the Palaeolithic archaeological record in conjunction with explicit assumptions about the processes behind, and interpretive potential of, the data being recorded.

With respect to handaxes, Wymer (1968) and Roe (1968, 1976, 1981) have emphasised the internal stylistic coherence of those few handaxe assemblages that have been collected under controlled conditions from known contexts, such as from the Middle Gravels at Swanscombe (Wymer 1968) and the Wolvercote Channel (cf. Tyldesley 1986). This point is reinforced by more recent studies of material from Boxgrove and Red Barns (Wenban-Smith 2000b). Given the careful attention to shaping in many of these handaxes, reflected in the removal of numerous minute chips and resulting in neat symmetrical and repeatedly similar forms, it is hard to imagine that their form does not correspond to a preconceived vision. Even workers such as White who generally regard the nature of the raw material blank as conditioning the final form of a handaxe, accept that certain forms such as twisted ovate were deliberately imposed (White 1998a). The fundamental premise can be adopted, therefore, that when a handaxe is knapped, its shape reflects a pre-conceived preference acquired within, and derived from the customary practice of, the social fabric of a network of interacting individuals (cf. Gamble 1993 & 1995), containing elements of form and technique which are deliberately imposed, whether consciously, or unconsciously through habit.

Given acceptance of the concept of imposed form in handaxes, and deliberately applied technological repertoires such as Levalloisian, further significant issues affecting the use of lithic artefacts for dating concern:

• *Cultural tradition*	The notion of cultural tradition and its relation to lithic production.
• *Range*	The spatial range of socially linked breeding communities, or population networks.
• *Technological variety*	The extent to which the material cultural output of a population network included varied handaxe forms and knapping strategies.
• *Technological texture*	The degree and spatial scale of homogeneity of technological output within the network range.
• *Stability*	The chronological scale over which spatial range and technological output varied.

Cultural tradition

One view of cultural tradition sees it as the deliberate practice of customs and production of specific artefacts that define a self-identifying group. In this sense, the "Clactonians" know they are Clactonians, and as such would always follow the established customs of core reduction, avoiding assiduously the manufacture of handaxes, except possibly as a flagrant destabilising revolutionary act. This caricature broadly reflects the 19th and early 20th century approach, and is widely derided. However, cultural tradition can also be used in the sense of a repertoire of common cultural practices socially acquired and transmitted within the context of a Palaeolithic population network. Such practices would not be deliberately intended to assert identity, but would merely reflect normal ways of doing things, learnt and transmitted through observation and emulation in the context of whatever range of situations led to lithic production. In this sense, a Clactonian cultural tradition merely reflects a shared technological repertoire dominated by the *ad hoc* manufacture of flakes from cores and a range of crude flake-tools, and lacking the habit of making handaxes.

Range

Such a population network would have operated within a particular region. Gamble & Steele (1999) have attempted to put some gross figures on the likely regional ranges of Lower and Middle Palaeolithic hominid groups, and, based on a combination of comparative mammalian studies and archaeological evidence from the sites of Arago and Grotte Vaufrey in France, have produced a figure of *c.* 1,000–2,000km^2, which equates roughly to a square with sides 30–45km or a circle of diameter 40–50km. This provides an initial ballpark figure for an idea of the spatial scale at which it might be appropriate to seek regional chronological sequences, at the same time as suggesting the futility of attempts to produce pan-British or pan-European sequences.

Technological variety

The variety and distinctiveness of the lithic technology and typology distributed by a group around its range has major implications for its subsequent recognition. One could postulate networks whose bifacial products were dominated by single forms, for instance pointed or ovate. Alternatively one could suggest a network that habitually made two functionally complementary forms of handaxe, for instance one very pointed and one very ovate. Or it is possible that handaxe shape was highly variable according to specific short-term functional/social needs. Additional potential complications are the nature or presence of any associated flake/core production: for instance an unstructured *ad hoc* approach, or a Levalloisian approach; and if Levalloisian then flake or blade, recurrent or linear.

The archaeological record can be of use here. It is clear from the assemblages from less disturbed and better provenanced sites that despite a certain amount of variation in size and refinement, there was usually a clear preference for specific handaxe forms and knapping approaches. Within the Boxgrove collection, which includes probably the largest and most tightly chronologically controlled handaxe assemblages excavated in Britain, there is a total absence of pointed handaxe forms with thicker, less worked butts, and a tiny amount of flake/core production. Conversely, pointed handaxes predominate in Wymer's (1964 & 1968) excavated assemblage from Swanscombe (Middle Gravels), and ovate forms similar to those from Boxgrove are absent. Handaxe assemblages from other sites such as Wolvercote, Red Barns and Hoxne (both Upper Industry and Lower Industry) are also generally dominated by specific shapes and repetitive technical approaches.

The argument could, however, be made that undisturbed sites, even those covering the area and time-span of Boxgrove, represent particular landscape contexts and their associated functions, leading to predominance of a certain handaxe shape. This presumes a) that the distinctive handaxe shapes recognisable in the Palaeolithic record are not functionally equivalent, and b) that lithic manufacture and discard is tied to the location of tool-use. While extremely pointed handaxes clearly have an optimum piercing function not shared with more rounded-edged forms, the majority of handaxes have both points and areas of rounded edge, and there is wide scope within this general bifacial construct for isochrestic variation between different shapes of similar functional adequacy. Nonetheless the possible mutual functional exclusivity of ovates and ficrons raises an interesting area for further research, first to investigate their functionality, and second investigate the facts of the spatial and chronological resolutions of assemblages

containing one, other or both forms. Re point b) there is evidence at sites such as Boxgrove and Red Barns for the transport of handaxes around the landscape away from their locations of manufacture, which suggests they were already shaped to accommodate whatever situations might arise. Furthermore, the consistency of handaxe shape in assemblages such as the Swanscombe Middle Gravels, which have been gathered from a wider catchment area than an undisturbed site, supports the concept of a preconceived shape preference, albeit subject to variation in size and refinement.

Therefore it seems reasonable to adopt, as a working premise — one which could easily be revised on the basis of field discoveries — a model in which Palaeolithic population networks did habitually have a restricted repertoire of preferred handaxe forms and/or flake/core knapping strategies. The form/s or strategy/ies of choice may have drifted through their social transmission, context and functional needs, and only occasionally may sufficiently distinctive shapes (twisted ovate or plano-convex) or techniques (Levalloisian) have arisen to be noticeable as distinct to one particular period in a region. A further empirical dimension to this issue is that, if a certain distinctive pattern of handaxe or knapping technique is repeatedly observed in deposits of one particular date in a proscribed region, one could reasonably infer, until proven otherwise, that that handaxe shape or knapping strategy has chronological implications, whether or not one accepts the range of premises outlined here to support the use of lithic typology and technology in dating.

Technological texture

One of the problems identified by L. and S. Binford (1966 & 1969) with the culture-historical paradigm was the heterogeneity of behaviour within a territory, and the consequent spatial variability of the archaeological record. Although the Binfords' analysis was aimed at explanation of broadly synchronous assemblages of different proportions of the same tool-types within a region, the same general approach could be expanded to cover assemblages of different tool-types (such as pointed or ovate dominant), or different knapping strategies (such as Levalloisian flake/core or handaxe dominant). This is indeed a problem if one is looking solely at undisturbed evidence from a restricted area. This has often been regarded as the most desirable because of its chronological integrity, but the occurrence of different situations or resources at different locations within the landscape *could* have created a correspondingly varied archaeological record, if one adopts a predominantly functional premise for typological and technological variability. However, such undisturbed sites are rare, and the great majority of the Lower and Middle Palaeolithic record consists of transported artefacts gathered and mixed by fluvial processes. Despite regular breast-beating over the consequently impoverished nature of this evidence, its disturbance paradoxically helps the Palaeolithic archaeologist by creating exactly the homogenous archaeological record that is needed to defuse this problem by gathering a representative sample of the material cultural output in the catchment range of the fluvial context in question, provided the scale of the catchment is sufficient to include the range of variability in lithic production.

Stability

The final problem to consider is the tension between the chronological scales of technological change and depositional formation. One of the notable features of the Lower/Middle Palaeolithic archaeological record is the longevity of the basic biface and flake/core repertoire. As mentioned above, undisturbed sites are generally associated with a distinctive and repetitive technological repertoire. These may, however, represent no more than a few hours activity. The unit 4b and 4c landsurfaces at Boxgrove, presumed to contain material from maybe up to 100 years (Roberts *et al.* 1997; Roberts & Parfitt 1999) are also notable for the consistent manufacture of ovate tranchet-sharpened handaxes. So it is reasonable to presume stasis in a technological repertoire over *c.* 2–4 generations. However, sedimentary units such as terrace formations represent tens of thousands of years, although it is uncertain over how long a period they actually formed, and to what extent they incorporate derived material predating the period of formation. Over such a long period a single population network with even a very slow rate of change in knapping behaviour could manifest a range of different cultural traditions. Thus single terrace formations could include typologically and technologically varied material representing the product over a long period of a single population network. However, if significant change is slow enough, irregular enough, or distinctive enough, as it generally appears to be, there is still the possibility of picking up meaningful chronological patterning from the study of terrace units.

Taken together therefore, and notwithstanding these recognised problems, these premises provide a basis for approaching a constrained region with widespread and chronologically differentiated fluvial deposits and seeking to investigate, initially, whether any patterns of typological and technological change emerge. If such patterning is found, then that would lead to an initial model for a regional chronological framework of lithic material cultural change, subject to further investigation and independent testing by more firmly rooted Quaternary scientific methods. If such a framework proved robust in the face of subsequent investigation, it could then in turn provide the basis for an investigation into the spatial range and chronological longevity of any distinctive cultural traditions, and by association their associated population networks.

RED BARNS

In the case of Red Barns, the nature and situation of the site were particularly suitable for this type of investigation. The site is located on the edge of the Solent River, on high ground overlooking what would have been the estuarine floodplain or delta towards its mouth. If plano-convex handaxes, several of which have been found out in the nearby Warsash area (Burkitt *et al.* 1939; Shackley 1970), could have been shown to be associated with a particular terrace of the Solent River, many of which are well mapped and spatially differentiated in the Southampton area *c.* 20km to the west, then that might have helped in dating the Red Barns site, which is not itself associated with any raised beach or fluvial deposits. Unfortunately, examination of a sample of handaxes from Solent terraces 3–6 (following the terrace nomenclature of Edwards *et al.* 1987) in the Southampton area failed to produce any sign of plano-convex handaxes, let alone a predominance in any one terrace.

This exercise did, however, demonstrate the great variety of handaxe shapes recovered from these terraces, as well as the recurring presence of shapes and technological oddities unfamiliar to the writer, more used to material from East Anglia and the Lower Thames. Consequently a second study was conducted, in which all the material from one locality in one terrace was examined to investigate the nature and typological/technological diversity represented. The site chosen for this study was Highfield, for three main reasons:

- The previous trawl of material had uncovered some interesting pieces with a Highfield provenance.
- There was a reasonably large collection of Highfield material readily accessible in the main Southampton City Museum.
- Published sources indicated a reasonably secure and restricted provenance for Highfield material (Dale 1896; Doughty 1978).

HIGHFIELD

Site provenance and stratigraphy

Highfield is a small area of Southampton, bounded to the west by Southampton Common and to the east

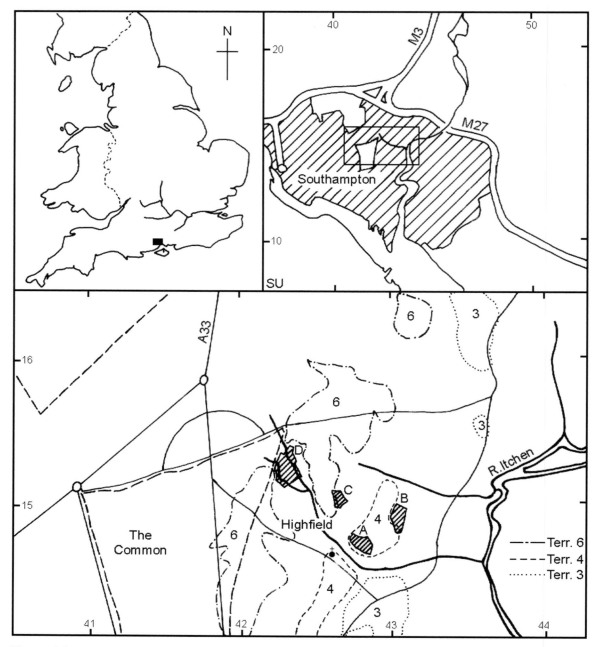

Figure 6.1: quarrying locations A–D in Highfield and Pleistocene terraces after Edwards et al. *(1987)*

by Portswood (Figure 6.1). It is centred on a pub, post-office and church, all with the epithet "Highfield", and at the junction of Highfield Lane, Highfield Avenue and Highfield Road, all of which are marked on OS maps of the early 20th century. It is hence a restricted and spatially well-defined locale. Figure 6.1 also shows the recent mapping of Pleistocene terraces (Edwards *et al.* 1987), with terraces 6, 4 and 3 all present in the Highfield area. The most common labelling for artefacts from the locale is just "Highfield", although several are labelled "Highfield Church", and two specimens are labelled "west of stream" and "Highfield Brick Pit" respectively. Quarrying has been carried out at four locations in the area since the first OS mapping

of the 19th century (Figure 6.1: A, B, C and D). Site A is beside the stream flowing immediately northeast of Highfield Church and clearly corresponds with the location where Dale (1896) reported the opening of a quarry and the recovery of over 100 artefacts. Site B is labelled as a "Brick Pit" on some OS maps, and is also marked on several as the location of a Palaeolithic floor found in 1915. Doughty's (1978) investigation confirmed that although some genuine artefacts were recovered at the site, most of the alleged artefacts from the "floor" are in fact unworked pieces of flint, which is an unfortunate irony since this continues to be the only site in Southampton where development has been halted to allow Palaeolithic excavation. Both sites A and B are dug into deposits from terrace 4.

Site C is only *c.* 300m to the north of site A, but is dug into the side of terrace 6. It is labelled as a "Sand Pit" on OS maps. There are no records of handaxe finds from the site, and Doughty reports that no finds were made during the construction of university buildings at the location, despite the presence of archaeologists looking for palaeoliths. Site D is labelled as a "Brick Pit and Yard". There are no records of finds from the site, and it is clear from the mapping that it is located in a place where the Pleistocene deposits of terrace 6 have been eroded through to the underlying Tertiary Bracklesham deposits, which constitute clays and sandy clays. These were presumably the target of the brick-making, so this site can also be discounted as a source of Highfield artefacts.

It seems safe, therefore, to presume that all Highfield artefacts came from terrace 4, and that the great majority came from the Highfield Church quarry. No records exist of the stratigraphy at the site, other than Dale's reference to "gravel". Doughty shows a section through the deposits at the Brick Pit at Site B based on a privately published pamphlet (Nicholas 1916). This shows a few feet of gravel capped by a horizontally laminated sandy and clayey horizon one foot thick. The deposits at Site A were probably thicker since it is closer to the valley side of the terrace, and one can provisionally assume that there was a single body of gravel which produced the artefacts at the site. Edwards *et al.*'s (1987) survey identifies the remaining deposits at Site A as being between 1 and 5 metres thick, and it is possible that fieldwork could re-expose the surviving deposits to clarify the stratigraphic sequence, as well as investigate for further artefacts.

Lithic assemblage

In total, 72 artefacts were examined, representing every artefact in the Southampton City Museum collection with a Highfield provenance. Their original source, in terms of collector, was unknown in most cases, although several specimens were identified as from the collections of Dale, Nicholas or Toogood. All of the artefacts were handaxes, which undoubtedly reflects collector bias, rather than a true indication of the archaeological content of the site. Their condition was recorded as one of four categories, mint, fresh, slightly rolled or very rolled (Table 6.1), and they were classified by shape following Wymer's (1968) scheme (Table 6.2).

The great majority of the handaxes were rolled, none were mint and only seven were fresh. This corresponds with the typical situation for material recovered from a fluvial gravel, where some artefacts get buried comparatively quickly with little damage, whereas others through chance get reworked more often and consequently battered more severely. There

was no indication from differential groups of condition, stain or patination that the collection represented anything other than a typical range from a single fluvial gravel context.

Category	Description	Number
Mint	As freshly knapped with edges razor sharp and tiny scars crisply defined	-
Fresh	Sharp to handle, with very slight damage/abrasion to sharp edges, ridges and scars	7
Slightly rolled	Some notching and battering of sharper edges, with ridges and scars slightly abraded	19
Very rolled	Intense notching and battering of all edges, plus heavy abrasion of ridges and flake scars	46

Table 6.1: condition of Highfield handaxes

The shapes of the handaxes were remarkably varied (Figures 6.2–6.3), with good examples of most of the different types recognised by Wymer. Figure 6.2 shows the four handaxes recorded specifically from the Highfield Church Pit; all four are generally pointed and two (ii and iv) are sufficiently pointed to qualify as ficrons. In the whole assemblage, the most common form (33%) was "classic pointed", over 4" long, straight-sided and well-made; and there were also eight classic ficrons (11%) with a sharp point and concave sides. Alongside these pointed forms was a range of more rounded and ovate forms, including sub-cordates (18%), ovates (18%), cleavers (7%) and a finely worked *bout coupé* specimen. The five handaxes shown in Figure 6.3 exemplify the variety of forms in this small assemblage, ranging from the extraordinary ficron of no. i, through the huge cleaver of no. ii to the perfectly circular disc of no. iv. The ficron measures 224mm from tip to base, which may place it amongst the 10 longest handaxes recorded in Britain, following the form-book of MacRae (1987).

Amongst the general variety, two particular stylistic or technical quirks recurred sufficiently frequently to become noticeable. First was the frequent presence of an elongated butt, usually left minimally or un-worked, for bluntly pointed and sub-cordate specimens (e.g. Figure 6.3(ii); Dale 1896, Plate I, no. 6). Dale (1896: 263) also describes this as a typical feature of Highfield implements. Second was the presence of three pointed handaxes of identical shape but varying size made by unifacial working of side-struck Levalloisian-like flakes (Figure 6.4).

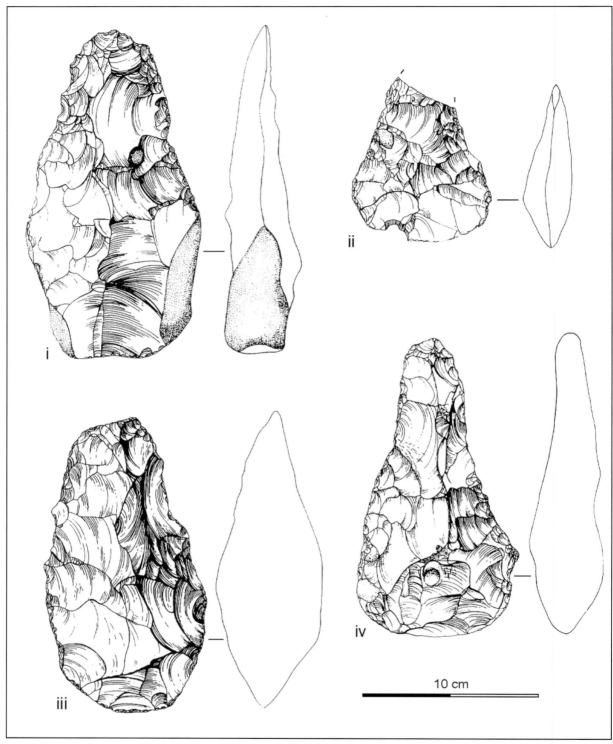

Figure 6.2: handaxes from Highfield Church Pit — i) narrow sub-cordate with minimally worked butt, ii) broken ficron, iii) narrow sub-cordate with worked butt, iv) ficron (illustrations by Barbara McNee)

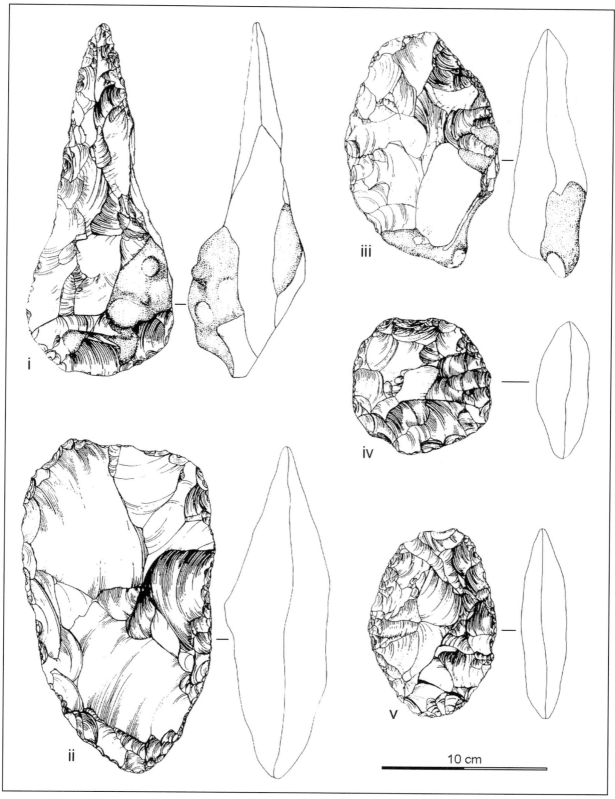

Figure 6.3: variety of handaxes from Highfield — i) ficron, ii) cleaver, iii) sub-cordate with elongated butt, iv) discoidal ovate, v) ovate (illustrations by Barbara McNee)

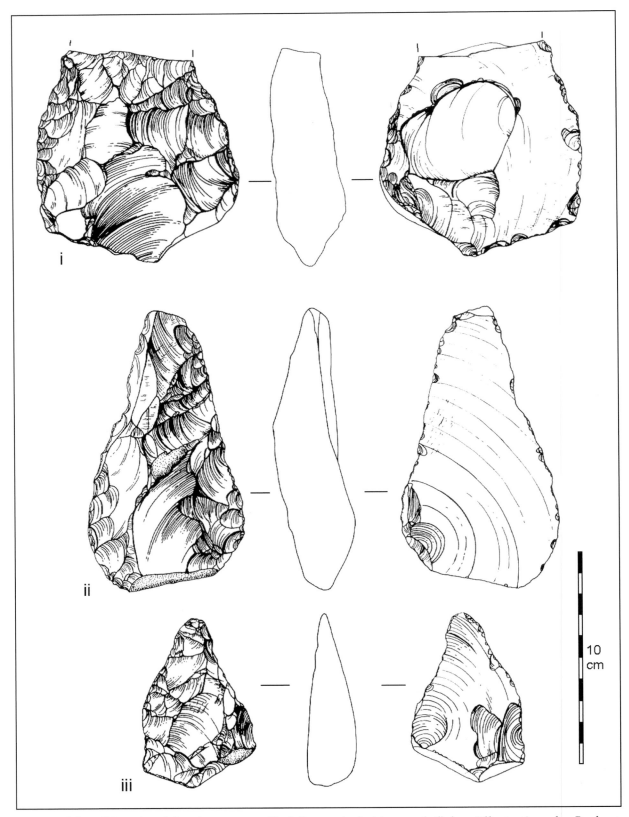

Figure 6.4: i–iii) pointed handaxes on unifacially worked side-struck flakes (illustrations by Barbara McNee)

Wymer type	Description	Number
-	Indeterminate	2
-	Rough-out \ abandoned	1
D	Large and crude	2
F	Classic pointed	24
G	Sub-cordate	13
H	Cleaver	5
K	Ovate	13
M	Classic ficron	8
N	Bout coupé	1
-	Pointed on side-struck flake	3
Total		72

Table 6.2: types of Highfield handaxes

DISCUSSION

The range of tool-types revealed in the Highfield assemblage does not conform neatly to the hoped-for model for Solent terraces, in which intra-terrace homogeneity would combine with inter-terrace heterogeneity to produce a nice framework of regional techno-typological change. This is, of course, only a tiny pilot study of a range of material whose common provenance is somewhat uncertain, and which has been undoubtedly subject to strong bias by collectors in their desire to retain distinctive and unusual specimens. It is however premature to write off the model outlined above on the basis of a sample from a single terrace, as a) it is possible that within the context of similar samples from other Solent terraces in Southampton, a pattern might emerge, and b) the range of material recovered could reflect unrecognised stratigraphic breaks in terrace 4, or the presence within terrace 4 of derived material from a sufficiently long period of time for significant changes in handaxe typology to have taken place. It is of course also possible that the suggested model is plain wrong, and that the variety of handaxe shapes produced reflects the varied repertoire of a single cultural tradition practiced by the population in the Solent region during the formation of terrace 4. As discussed above, more controlled recovery of material from fluvial terrace units has usually produced more typologically coherent assemblages. Furthermore, the two typological/technological quirks recognised may be just the sort of stylistically distinctive but functionally insignificant variation that could serve as a type-fossil for a particular period in a region *subject to a basis in further research*. If sufficient evidence is produced to both undermine the premises on which it is based and to confirm that such a regional model does not correspond with the patterning of the archaeological record, then that's science.

The most obvious source of such evidence would be further examination of assemblages from specific locations and horizons within fluvial terrace deposits. If an improved understanding of the spatial and chronological texture of Lower/Middle Palaeolithic material culture is to be developed, then a key area for further research has to be the investigation of the depositional processes associated with the formation of the river terrace deposits that contain the bulk of the evidence. Knowledge in three main areas — catchment range, timescale of deposition, extent of secondary derivation — is fundamental in assessing, for instance, whether an artefact assemblage represents i) a local sample from a short time-span in one part of a population range ii) a homogenised sample from a single population and cultural tradition across its range, or iii) a homogenised sample across such a long time-span that it may embrace significant technological change within the cultural tradition of a single population network. Only in the light of such basic facts can further progress be made in assessing the relative reasonableness of the many behavioural premises that must underlie any interpretation of lithic material.

CONCLUSIONS

Despite the richness of material from the Solent region, little research has been carried out, and no synthesis has been produced of typological and technological characteristics and change within the well-mapped Solent River terrace system. The impetus for such work may have been diminished following the collapse of Wymer's pan-British model based on Thames terrace deposits, based on anachronistic results from High Lodge, Hoxne and Boxgrove. However, if one takes account of the likely sub-national scale of meaningful patterning, it is possible that finer-grained research at a regional scale could bring hitherto unsuspected patterning into focus. The preliminary study carried out here, although producing highly varied material from a single terrace unit, also produced stylistically distinct technological and typological quirks which could serve as a basis for recognising a distinct phase in the Lower/Middle Palaeolithic of the Solent basin.

ACKNOWLEDGEMENTS

I am very grateful to Duncan Brown and Karen Wardley of the Southampton City Museum service for their help in finding the Highfield material in their store, allowing me to spend time studying it and letting me borrow pieces for illustration. Thanks are also due to my co-editor Rob Hosfield for tolerating the late appearance of this paper and for helpful comments on an early draft, although I take full responsibility for all its remaining inadequacies. Finally, a great debt of gratitude is owed to Barbara McNee for finding the time to diversify from penguins and produce the lithic illustrations.

___

REFERENCES

Ashton, N.M, Cook, J., Lewis, S.G. & Rose, J. (ed's). 1992. *High Lodge: excavations by G. de G. Sieveking 1962–68 and J. Cook 1988*. British Museum Press, London.

Ashton, N. & McNabb, J. 1994. Bifaces in perspective. In N. Ashton & A. David (ed's) *Stories in stone*: 182–191. Lithic Studies Society Occasional Paper No. 4. Lithic Studies Society, London.

Binford, L.R. 1983. *In Pursuit of the Past*. Thames and Hudson, New York.

Binford, L.R. & Binford, S.R. 1966. A preliminary analysis of functional variability in the Mousterian of Levallois facies. *American Anthropologist* 68(2): 238–95.

Binford, S.R. & Binford, L.R. 1969. Stone tools and human behaviour. *Scientific American* 220: 70–84.

Bradley, B. & Sampson, C.G. 1986. Analysis by replication of two Acheulian artefact assemblages. In G. Bailey & P. Callow (ed's) *Stone Age Prehistory: Studies in Honour of Charles McBurney*: 29–45. Cambridge University Press, Cambridge.

Breuil, H. & L. Koslowski. 1931. Etudes de stratigraphie Paléolithique dans le nord de la France, la Belgique et l'Angleterre: la vallée de la Somme. *L'Anthropologie* 41: 449–488.

Breuil, H. & L. Koslowski. 1932. Etudes de stratigraphie Paléolithique dans le nord de la France, la Belgique et l'Angleterre: V — basse terrasse de la Somme. *L'Anthropologie* 42: 27–47 & 291–314.

Bridgland, D.R. 1996. Quaternary river terrace deposits as a framework for the Lower Palaeolithic record. In C.S. Gamble and A.J. Lawson (ed's) *The English Palaeolithic Reviewed*: 24–39. Trust for Wessex Archaeology, Salisbury.

Burkitt, M.C., Paterson, T.T. & Mogridge, C.J. 1939. The Lower Palaeolithic industries near Warsash, Hampshire. *Proceedings of the Prehistoric Society* 5: 39–50.

Dale, W. 1896. The Palaeolithic implements of the Southampton gravels. *Papers and Proceedings of the Hampshire Field Club* 3: 261–264.

Dibble, H.L. 1987. The interpretation of Middle Paleolithic scraper morphology. *American Antiquity* 52: 109–117.

Doughty, R.M. 1978. *An Analysis of the Spatial and Temporal Distribution of Palaeoliths from Southampton*. Unpublished BA dissertation, Department of Archaeology, University of Southampton.

Edwards, R.A., Scrivener, R.C. & Forster, A. 1987. *Applied Geological Mapping: Southampton Area*. Research Report of the British Geological Survey, No. ICSO/87/2. British Geological Survey, Exeter.

Gamble, C.S. 1993. Exchange, foraging and local hominid networks. In C. Scarre & F. Healy (ed's) *Trade and Exchange in Prehistoric Europe*: 35–44. Oxbow Books, Oxford.

Gamble, C.S. 1995. Making tracks: hominid networks and the evolution of the social landscape. In J. Steele & S. Shennan (ed's) *The Archaeology of Human Ancestry: Power, Sex and Tradition*: 253–277. Routledge, London.

Gamble, C.S. & Steele, J. 1999. Hominid ranging patterns and dietary strategies. In H. Ullrich (ed.) *Hominid Evolution: Lifestyles and survival strategies*: 396–409.

Archea, Schwelm.

Kohn, M. & Mithen, S. 1999. Handaxes: products of sexual selection? *Antiquity* 73: 518–526.

MacRae, R.J. 1987. The great giant handaxe stakes. *Lithics* 8: 15–17.

de Mortillet, G. & A. 1900. *Le Préhistorique Origine et Antiquité de l'Homme* (3rd edition). Reinwald, Paris.

Nicholas, R.E. 1916. Record of a Prehistoric Industry in Tabular Flint at Brambridge and Highfield.

Roberts, M.B. & Parfitt, S.A. 1999. *Boxgrove: a Middle Pleistocene hominid site at Eartham Quarry, Boxgrove, West Sussex*: 395–415. English Heritage Archaeological Report 17. English Heritage, London.

Roberts, M.B., Parfitt, S.A., Pope, M.I & Wenban-Smith, F.F. 1997. Boxgrove, West Sussex: rescue excavations of a Lower Palaeolithic landsurface (Boxgrove Project B, 1989–91). *Proceedings of the Prehistoric Society* 63: 303–358.

Roberts, M.B., Stringer, C.B. & Parfitt, S.A. 1994. A hominid tibia from Middle Pleistocene sediments at Boxgrove, UK. *Nature* 369: 311–313.

Roe, D.A. 1968. British Lower and Middle Palaeolithic handaxe groups. *Proceedings of the Prehistoric Society* 34: 1–82.

Roe, D.A. 1976. Typology and the trouble with handaxes. In G. de G. Sieveking, I.H. Longworth & K.E. Wilson (ed's) *Problems in economic and social archaeology*: 61–70. Duckworth, London.

Roe, D.A. 1981. *The Lower and Middle Palaeolithic periods in Britain*. Routledge & Kegan Paul, London.

Shackley, M.L. 1970. Preliminary note on handaxes found in gravel deposits at Warsash, Hampshire. *Proceedings of the Hants Field Club Archaeological Society* 27: 5–7.

Shackley, M.L. 1977. The *bout coupé* handaxe as a typological marker for the British Mousterian industries. In R.V.S. Wright (ed.) *Stone Tools as Cultural Markers*: 332–339. Australian Institute of Aboriginal Studies, Canberra.

Tyldesley, J.A. 1986. *The Wolvercote Channel Handaxe Assemblage: a Comparative Study*. BAR British Series 153. British Archaeological Reports, Oxford.

Tyldesley, J.A. 1987. *The Bout Coupé handaxe: a typological problem*. BAR British Series 170. British Archaeological Reports, Oxford.

Wenban-Smith, F.F. 1998. Clactonian and Acheulian industries in Britain: their chronology and significance reconsidered. In N. Ashton, F. Healy & P. Pettitt (ed's) *Stone Age Archaeology: Essays in Honour of John Wymer*: 90–97. Oxbow Books, Oxford.

Wenban-Smith, F.F. 2000a. Technology and typology. In F.F. Wenban-Smith, C.S. Gamble & A.M. ApSimon. The Lower Palaeolithic site at Red Barns, Portchester, Hampshire: bifacial technology, raw material quality and the organisation of Archaic behaviour. *Proceedings of the Prehistoric Society* 66: 209–255.

Wenban-Smith, F.F. 2000b. Lithic artefacts. In F.F. Wenban-Smith, C.S. Gamble & A.M. ApSimon. The Lower Palaeolithic site at Red Barns, Portchester, Hampshire: bifacial technology, raw material quality and the organisation of Archaic behaviour. *Proceedings of the Prehistoric Society* 66: 209–255.

Wenban-Smith, F.F., Gamble C.S. & ApSimon, A.M. 2000. The Lower Palaeolithic site at Red Barns, Portchester, Hampshire: bifacial technology, raw material quality and the organisation of Archaic behaviour. *Proceedings of the Prehistoric Society* 66: 209–255.

White, M.J. 1998a. Twisted ovate bifaces in the British Lower Palaeolithic: some observations and implications. In N. Ashton, F. Healy & P. Pettitt (ed's) *Stone Age Archaeology: Essays in Honour of John Wymer*: 98–104. Oxbow Books, Oxford.

White, M.J. 1998b. On the significance of Acheulean biface variability in southern Britain. *Proceedings of the Prehistoric Society* 64: 15–44.

White, M.J. 2000. The Clactonian question: on the interpretation of core-and-flake assemblages in the British Lower Palaeolithic. *Journal of World Prehistory* 14: 1–63.

Wymer, J.J. 1964. Excavations at Barnfield Pit, 1955–1960. In C.D. Ovey (ed.) *The Swanscombe Skull: a Survey of Research on a Pleistocene Site*: 19–61. Occasional Paper No. 20. Royal Anthropological Institute, London.

Wymer, J.J. 1968. *Lower Palaeolithic Archaeology in Britain as Represented by the Thames Valley*. John Baker, London.

Wymer, J.J. 1974. Clactonian and Acheulian industries in Britain — their chronology and significance. *Proceedings of the Geologists Association* 85: 391–421.

Wymer, J.J. 1983. The Lower Palaeolithic site at Hoxne. *Proceedings of the Suffolk Institute of Archaeology and History* 35: 169–189.

7. PRIORY BAY, ISLE OF WIGHT: A REVIEW OF CURRENT KNOWLEDGE

R.D. Loader

ABSTRACT

Palaeolithic implements were first found on the shore at Priory Bay on the northeast coast of the Isle of Wight in the late nineteenth century. Since then, more than 500 handaxes have been recovered by local collectors, and material has been found in situ *in gravel at the top of the cliff, but the site has yet to be properly investigated.*

INTRODUCTION

The Isle of Wight is best known for the Palaeolithic assemblage from Great Pan Farm (IWSMR 877), near Newport, which was collected during gravel digging in the early part of the twentieth century (Poole 1925), and which contains implements of Mousterian type (Shackley 1973; Wymer 1999). Gravel extraction at Bleak Down (IWSMR 827) in the southern part of the Island also produced Palaeolithic artefacts (Poole 1931). The Isle of Wight SMR records a general scatter of stray finds of this period which have a largely coastal distribution (Figure 7.1), but the largest collection of material has been made at Priory Bay (IWSMR 1192), a site that has been producing Palaeolithic implements for over a century.

LOCATION

Priory Bay is located on the northeast coast of the Island, to the north of Bembridge Harbour and south of Seaview (Figure 7.2). It is a shallow north–south orientated bay, which is delimited by outcrops of Bembridge limestone at Horestone Point at its north end and Nodes Point to the south. The bay is backed by a steep coastal slope which comprises a series of rotational slumps. This is fronted at the southern end by the remains of a substantial sea wall which was built in the early twentieth century but which is now severely damaged. At the top of the cliff, Nodes Point Battery, built in the late 1800s, now serves as a holiday camp, with chalets extending to the edge of the coastal slope.

The steep slope is heavily wooded and overgrown. Photographs taken at the time of the first discoveries show it to be largely unwooded but trees were planted in the early twentieth century in an attempt to stabilise the coastal slope. This vegetation has obscured the gravel deposits at the top of the cliff where the early collectors found worked flints *in situ*.

The majority of Palaeolithic material has been found on the beach below, and finds are concentrated in a small area at the southern end of the bay where the eroding slope is spilling onto the beach (Figure 7.2).

SITE HISTORY

Priory Bay was one of the first Palaeolithic sites to be recognised on the Isle of Wight. The first implement was found by Professor E.B. Poulton in 1888 on the shore to the east of Horestone Point. By 1902 implements had also been found in gravel which had fallen from the exposures at the top of the cliff, and in the same year a handaxe was found *in situ* in the cliff face. Prolific finds were also made on the beach below, and by 1909, 150 implements had been recovered. These finds were published by R.W. Poulton (1909). His report includes photographs which show some of the implements found *in situ* at the top of the cliff to be in very fresh condition. The Poulton collection was subsequently deposited at the Pitt Rivers Museum in Oxford.

Poulton described the deposits from which the implements were recovered: "The locality which has

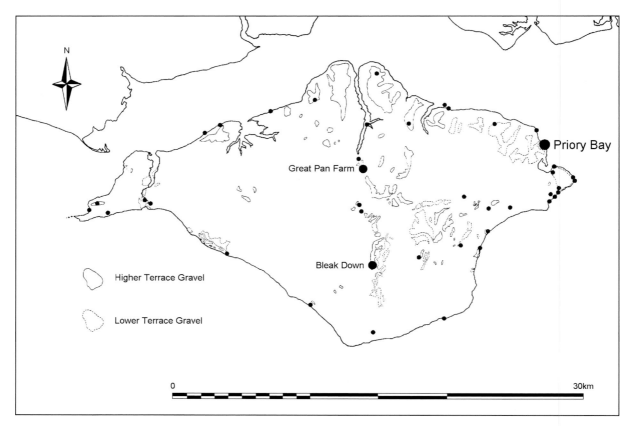

Higher Terrace Gravel

Lower Terrace Gravel

0   30km

Figure 7.1: Isle of Wight Palaeolithic find-spots (after Wymer 1999 with later additions)

yielded the most plentiful traces of Palaeolithic man is a large gravel section, close to the sea, at the south end of Priory Bay. The gravel face is about 12 feet high (including overlying earth) and 120 yards long. It rests on the Bembridge Clays. On both sides trees and shrubs effectively limit the field of search. The gravel is clearly stratified, and includes several bands of gravely clay. Many of these implements must have been buried in these bands, and it is to this cause that we owe the almost perfect preservation of so many of the specimens" (Poulton 1909: 39). He added, "Those found at the section are mostly quite unworn, sharp and unabraded. A few, however are very much abraded as if they had been worn in some former river bed" (*ibid.* 40). Unfortunately he did not include section drawings or photographs of the deposits in which the implements were found.

In the early part of the twentieth century the site was also visited regularly by Hubert Poole, a local antiquarian, who was responsible for initial investigations at Bleak Down and Great Pan Farm. He made his own collection of flintwork, including both material he picked up himself and that found by workmen who were engaged in digging drainage ditches on the coastal slope in an attempt to curb the rapid erosion. Poole also made notes and took photographs of the beach and the gravel capping the top of the cliff. His manuscripts and the implements that he collected are now housed at the Isle of Wight County Archaeological Centre (Poole undated manuscript).

More recently a large collection of flints was made by a local man, Mr. Brian Elcox, who recovered more than 300 artefacts from the beach (Figure 7.3). His collection, most of which has been donated to the Isle of Wight County Archaeological Collection, was examined by Samson as part of an undergraduate dissertation in the 1970s. She concluded that the material included both Acheulian and Mousterian of Acheulian Tradition types (Samson 1976). This conclusion was based on the size and refinement of the implements, and their degree of abrasion. Implements with abrasion indices greater than 0.5mm were classed as Acheulian, and those with lower index values as Mousterian. The 'Acheulian' assemblage was correlated with Roe's group VII, an ovate tradition with a high percentage of tranchet finish and rare twisted profiles, and the 'Mousterian' assemblage was considered to be similar to Roe's group VI, subgroup C, a highly refined group in which pointed ovates, twisted profiles and tranchet finish were common (Roe 1968). Samson felt that the material represented a true assemblage rather than a random accumulation because handaxes, retouched flakes and débitage were all present. Since this assessment was made, significantly more material has been recovered from Priory Bay and the assemblage now warrants re-examination.

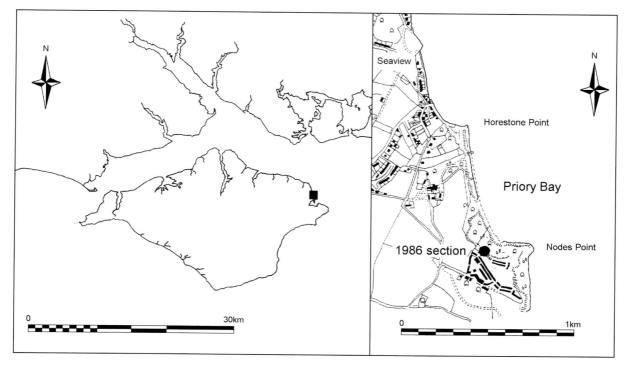

Figure 7.2: the location of Priory Bay and the 1986 excavation

THE EXCAVATION

In 1986 a section was cut at the top of the cliff as part of what was then the Nature Conservancy Council's geological site cleaning programme. The purpose of this excavation was to record the stratigraphy and isolate any Palaeolithic artefacts within the sequence. A suitable site was identified at SZ 6351 8996, where a gravel face was partly obscured by slumped material at the top of the coastal slope adjacent to the Nodes Point Holiday Camp.

A section approximately 1.75m wide was cleaned of the loose material which was obscuring the section. Thirty-eight humanly struck flint flakes were recovered during this operation. The condition of these flakes ranged enormously from very fresh material which was unlikely to be of Palaeolithic date, to highly rolled and patinated flakes, and they included possible handaxe roughing-out and thinning flakes (Newcomer 1971).

The cleaned section revealed 4.49 metres of sediment overlying the Bembridge marls. The sequence was initiated by coarse sand, the base at 29.12m O.D., overlain by gravels, sands and finally a little over a metre of brickearth (Figure 7.4). A heavily rolled, bifacially worked implement was found *in situ* in coarse gravel at *c.* 31.5m O.D. (Figure 7.5). The degree of abrasion and patination displayed on this piece was similar to the more highly rolled examples which had been recovered from the beach.

The gravel in which the implement was found was mainly sub-angular and sub-rounded in character and was dominated by flint with minor inclusions of quartz, chert, ironstone and chalk (M. Munt pers.

comm.). A rounded clast of granite was found in the material which had fallen from the section and was assumed to have come from the gravel (Preece *et al.* 1990).

There has been considerable debate as to whether the Priory Bay gravels are of marine or fluviatile origin, and how the deposits relate to the Bembridge raised beach which is exposed in the cliff face some 3–4 km to the south of Priory Bay (Preece & Scourse 1987; Preece *et al.* 1990). This uncertainty is due in part to the considerable differences both in the character and the height O.D. between the gravels at Priory Bay and the Bembridge raised beach. However, it has recently been concluded that the deposit at Priory Bay is raised beach gravel (Bridgland 1999: 108). The low degree of rounding and the scarcity of non-flint material in the Priory Bay gravels compared with the Bembridge raised beach is explained by the fact that Priory Bay is in a comparatively more sheltered position within the mouth of the Solent estuary.

CONCLUSION

Although only a very small section of the cliff face at Priory Bay was examined in 1986, the amount of worked flint found was encouraging. It is well known that the early collectors had recovered material from *in situ* in the gravel at the top of the cliff, but this was the first time that the precise location of an implement and the site stratigraphy had been recorded. The occurrence of a very abraded

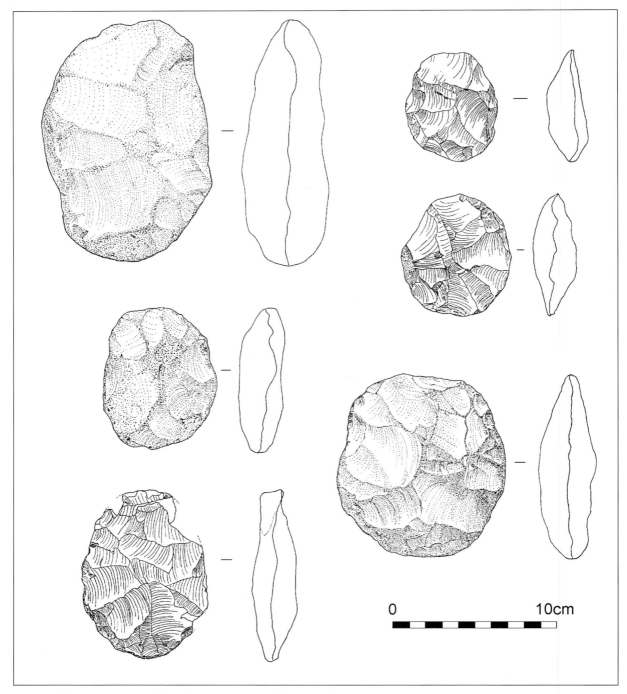

Figure 7.3: a selection of handaxes recovered from the beach at Priory Bay

implement *in situ* in the cliff section suggests that the wide variety in the condition of the artefacts which have been found at the base of the cliff is probably an accurate reflection of their original condition and is not necessarily due to some having been subjected to erosional processes on the beach for longer than others.

Implements and struck flakes are still regularly being recovered from the beach at Priory Bay. Almost 900 worked flints, including 130 handaxes, are now housed in the Isle of Wight County Archaeological Collection. Finds are still concentrated at the southern end of the bay where the slumped cliff spills onto the beach. An unabraded handaxe was found in this area by Mr. Alan Brading in 1996, and two more handaxes were found recently in the northern part of the bay.

The site at Priory Bay is under constant threat from coastal erosion. The remains of the sea wall are in very poor condition and offer little protection from the force of the waves. The slumped material at the foot of the cliff is eroding rapidly and as a consequence the base of the cliff is becoming

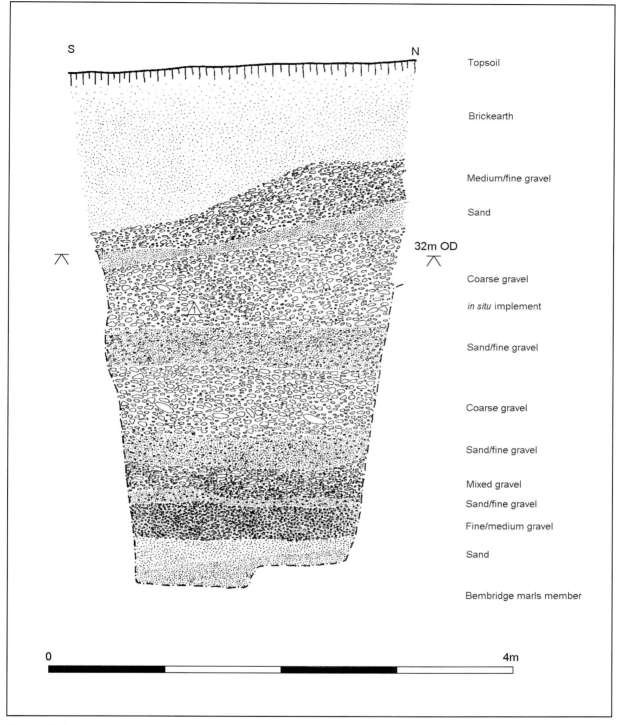

Figure 7.4: section excavated at the top of the cliff at Priory Bay in 1986

steepened. It is likely that this steepening may soon set off a further sequence of erosion and slumping.

As a result of the importance of the gravels and the Palaeolithic material contained within them, the coastal slope at Priory Bay has now been made a Site of Special Scientific Interest. However, this designation does not protect the material *in situ* at the top of the cliff, which is still under pressure both from coastal erosion and from the expansion of tourism.

In spite of the large numbers of artefacts which continue to be recovered from Priory Bay and the potential importance of the deposits which contain them, the site is still poorly understood. As long ago as 1980, investigative work at Priory Bay was viewed as a priority (Basford 1980: 79), a recommendation that was endorsed by the Southern Rivers Palaeolithic Project (Wessex Archaeology 1992). The excavation of 1986 succeeded in tracing the implements to the

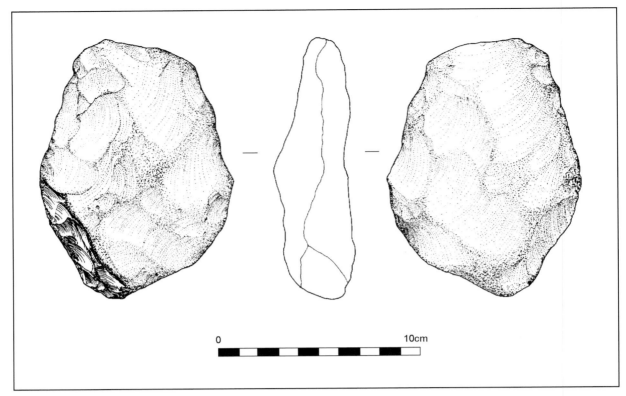

Figure 7.5: implement found in situ *during the excavation of 1986*

gravels at the top of the cliff, and a series of similar small-scale evaluations would allow the site stratigraphy to be extrapolated in greater detail. The presence of the unrolled artefacts that were recorded by Poulton (1909) suggests that material survives in a less disturbed context than has yet been traced. The position of the site at the top of an eroding coastal slope means that the deposits are comparatively easily accessible and sections can be viewed by removing the talus material without the necessity of excavating large amounts of overburden. In addition to conducting further fieldwork, a reassessment of the lithic assemblage that has already been recovered from the site is also long overdue.

REFERENCES

Basford, H.V. 1980. *The Vectis Report: a Survey of Isle of Wight Archaeology*. Isle of Wight County Council, Newport.

Bridgland, D.R. 1999. Analysis of the raised beach gravel deposits at Boxgrove and related sites. In M.B. Roberts & S.A. Parfitt (ed's) *Boxgrove: a Middle Pleistocene Hominid Site at Eartham Quarry, Boxgrove, West Sussex*: 100–111. English Heritage, London.

Newcomer, M.H. 1971. Some quantitative experiments in hand-axe manufacture. *World Archaeology* 3: 85–94.

Poole, H.F. 1925. Palaeoliths from Great Pan Farm. *Proceedings of the Hampshire Field Club and Archaeological Society* 9: 305–319.

Poole, H.F. 1931. Gravel and flint implements of Bleak Down. *Proceedings of the Hampshire Field Club and Archaeological Society* 12: 20–47.

Poole, H.F. Undated manuscript. *Palaeolithic*. Unpublished manuscript, Isle of Wight County Archaeological Collection.

Poulton, R.W. 1909. An account of discoveries of Palaeolithic implements in the Isle of Wight. In F. Morey (ed.) *A Guide to the Natural History of the Isle of Wight*: 37–41. Isle of Wight County Press, Newport.

Preece, R.C. & Scourse, J.D. 1987. Pleistocene sea-level history in the Bembridge area of the Isle of Wight. In K. E. Barber (ed.) *Wessex and the Isle of Wight: Field Guide*: 136–149. Quaternary Research Association, Cambridge.

Preece, R.C., Scourse, J.D., Houghton, S.D., Knudsen, K.L. & Penney, D.N. 1990. The Pleistocene sea-level and neotectonic history of the Eastern Solent, Southern England. *Philosophical Transactions of the Royal Society of London Series B 328*: 425–477.

Roe, D.A. 1968. British Lower and Middle Palaeolithic handaxe groups. *Proceedings of the Prehistoric Society* 34: 1–82.

Samson, F.R. 1976. *Priory Bay: a Study of an Unstratified Palaeolithic Site in the Isle of Wight*. Unpublished Undergraduate dissertation, University of Southampton.

Shackley, M.L. 1973. A contextual study of the Mousterian industry from Great Pan Farm, Newport, Isle of Wight. *Proceedings of the Isle of Wight Natural History and Archaeological Society* 6: 542–554.

Wessex Archaeology. 1992. *The Upper Thames Valley, the Kennet Valley and the Solent Drainage System: the Southern Rivers Palaeolithic Project, Report no. 1, 1991–1992*. Wessex Archaeology, Salisbury.

Wymer, J. J. 1999. *The Lower Palaeolithic Occupation of Britain*. Wessex Archaeology, Salisbury.

8. THE BROOM PITS: A REVIEW OF RESEARCH AND A PILOT STUDY OF TWO ACHEULIAN BIFACE ASSEMBLAGES

G.D. Marshall

ABSTRACT

Located along the eastern bank of the River Axe in Devon, the Broom gravel pits have from at least the late nineteenth century, produced significant numbers of Acheulian bifaces made of Greensand chert. Although similar to flint in many respects, the use of this raw material provides an interesting contrast to the predominance of the latter within most assemblages from Southern England. Recent work by Ashton & McNabb (1993) and White (1998) has emphasised the role played by raw materials on biface form. It is with this in mind that the use of Greensand chert is discussed, in particular the effects of raw material quality and nodule size on artefact form.

INTRODUCTION

Gravel quarrying along the River Axe has produced significant numbers of bifaces in various states of preservation since the mid nineteenth century. However, mechanisation, the decline in extraction and the shallowness of recent diggings has resulted in only a handful of discoveries since around 1950. Two assemblages in particular make up most of what are referred to as the Broom collections, those from the Old Ballast and Holditch Lane pits. The Old Ballast Pit was operational from the mid nineteenth century and was collected from by Worthington Smith, Christy and Sturge amongst others. The Holditch Lane pits were developed during the nineteen thirties and were investigated by the local amateur archaeologist Charles Bean. The Axe gravels and biface collections from Broom in particular represent the most significant north-westerly extent of the Acheulian world, finds further north and west are small scale in comparison. This extreme visibility, although in part probably reflecting the use of chert gravels, points to repeated activity along the Axe and its tributaries. This stenotopic or tethered behaviour is typical of the Acheulian generally (Deacon & Deacon 1999: 81), and goes some way towards explaining the density of finds along the Axe. Broom represents one of the most significant non-flint using sites in much of north western Europe at least, although both flint and chert behave in similar ways when worked. The presence at Broom of well preserved polleniferous clays, fresh artefacts and concentrations of thirty or more bifaces in close proximity to one another suggests the possibility of intact deposits (Green 1988: 180). The potential presence of *in situ* deposits, the well documented biface collection from the Holditch Lane pits in particular, the unique location of Broom and use of chert, all point towards the value of undertaking further work at Broom.

AIMS

This paper forms part of a pilot study for work being initiated at Broom, and in particular a re-analysis of Charles Bean's Holditch Lane collection (Marshall in prep.). The aim is to review work undertaken along the Axe since the mid nineteenth century, and then to investigate the significance if any, of fresh and rolled bifaces amongst the two largest Broom collections. The final aim is to consider possible long distance transport of flint and chert between Hampshire and the West Country.

HISTORY OF RESEARCH

In 1897 Sir John Evans wrote of the discovery sometime before 1870 of four bifaces along the River Axe (Evans 1897). By this time gravel extraction was well underway around the small hamlet of Broom, having begun sometime around 1850 (Reid Moir 1933: 264). Early quarrying work was concentrated at the Old Ballast Pit located along the south bank of the Blackwater just south of Broom. In a paper in the Geological Magazine, W. S. D'Urban reported on the presence of both fresh and rolled implements (1878: 37), and these were again noted by Salter in the Geological Survey Memoirs of 1906.

During the 1930s, a new series of pits were opened along the Holditch Lane within the hamlet of Broom itself, and remained in operation until around 1947 (Green 1988: 173). The largest lay along the northern edge of the Holditch Lane and was referred to as New Pit (Hawkes 1943: 49) and then Pratt's Old Pit (Green 1988: 174). It was from here that a substantial collection of between 900 and 1000 bifaces was made during the 1930s and early 1940s by Charles Bean, the Borough surveyor and local amateur archaeologist. Along with detailed records and a survey of the pit, Bean undertook an analysis of his biface collection, although these were never published. It was left to Reid Moir (1936), who on the basis of a series of visits to the Holditch Lane pits with Bean during 1935 and 1936, published a useful paper on the artefacts and deposits. The site was again discussed by Hawkes (1943), and more recently by Shakesby & Stephens (1984), and in a useful paper by Green (1988) in which the results of Bean's 1942 analysis are presented. Summaries of the artefacts and descriptions of the site have been included in the Southern Rivers' volumes (Wessex Archaeology 1993: 159) and Wymer (1999: 181–185).

Gravel extraction along the Axe has always been small scale, with a single pit remaining in operation at Chard Junction. Applications for three new extraction areas have recently been granted and according to the site owners, Aggregate Industries, these are expected to remain in operation for fifteen to twenty years (Fowler pers. comm.). However, extraction is unlikely to extend down to the current floodplain of the Axe, a level at which the Broom quarries just under two miles downstream produced the majority of their artefacts.

LOCATION AND GEOLOGY

The majority of collections attributed to Broom were derived from two main pits. The first, Old Ballast Pit, Railway Pit or Hawkchurch lies just south of the Blackwater River, a tributary of the Axe, and a few hundred meters south of the hamlet of Broom. The second, Pratt's Old Pit or Thorncombe is located north of the Holditch Lane within Broom itself. Although only a few hundred meters apart, the two pits are located in different counties. The boundary between Devon and Dorset runs east to west along the Blackwater and then north along the Axe. The Old Ballast Pit is therefore located in Devon, while Pratt's Holditch Lane workings are located in Dorset.

Although presently small, the Axe meanders within a large floodplain of up to half a kilometre in width, and is flanked on either side by steep gravel capped hills. It is these that have been quarried since the mid nineteenth century (Reid Moir 1936: 264). The surrounding landscape is extensively incised due to erosion of the softer chalk and greensand which together comprise the westerly extent of the Cretaceous in the area. To the west lie the much older Triassic and Permian of Devon and Cornwall.

The Axe gravels are composed primarily of Cretaceous flint and chert, the origin of which has been interpreted in two ways. Either as fluvio-glacial outwash from an ice margin north of Chard Gap (Stephens 1970, 1974, 1977; Shakesby & Stephens 1984), or alternatively as the result of local erosion of remnant Tertiary deposits and *in situ* cherts (Green 1974). The lack of erratics and any firm evidence for glacial deposits in the Somerset Levels suggests local erosion as a more likely mechanism (Shakesby & Stephens 1984: 84). Along with smaller fractions, chert within the deposits occur as large lightly rolled blocks, some up to 35cm in length. In the Aggregate Industries pit at Chard Junction, flint was present but at low density, rare examples measuring up to 12cm in diameter although the majority were much smaller. Grainy and frost fractured, those large enough for biface manufacture were estimated to comprise less than five percent of the deposit. Pollen analysis from clays and silts overlying the principle artefact horizon in the Old Ballast pit have suggested overbank sedimentation, possibly during the Hoxnian or an interstadial within the Wolstonian (Green pers. comm.; Shakesby & Stephens 1984: 87).

THE BROOM BIFACE COLLECTIONS

The collections

The Broom collections number many thousands of bifaces and are widely dispersed within national, local and university museum collections. Old Ballast Pit bifaces from the Worthington Smith, Christy and Sturge collections are held by the British Museum while the Holditch Lane collection of Charles Bean is dispersed amongst a number of local and university museums (Green pers. comm.). The bulk of the artefacts from both collections appear to have been derived from the iron stained red beds between 45.5m

O.D. and 49.75m O.D., at roughly the same level as the present floodplain of the Axe, currently at 45m O.D. (Green 1988: 180). The two assemblages are similar and consist of a range of cleavers, ovates and pointed types of both flint and chert. Although flint was being used, chert was by far the most common. Only 4.3% (n=11) of a sample of 239 bifaces from the Old Ballast Pit were of flint, while in Bean's collection of 899 artefacts from Holditch Lane, flint comprised just over 3% (n=28) (Green 1988: 177).

Aims of the biface study

In his original 1942 study of the Broom handaxes, Bean noted the presence of both rolled and fresh artefacts. The fact that most of the collection was derived from within a single two meter thick horizon (Green 1988: 178) suggests that the rolled component was either being moved from elsewhere or alternatively that earlier deposits were being reworked. The implication is of a possible spatial or temporal separation between the fresh and rolled assemblages. It is the aim of the following analysis to investigate whether any such disjunction can be identified between the fresh and rolled components of the two collections. The study begins with a discussion of Bean's 1942 analysis of the Holditch Lane bifaces as summarised by Green (1988), and is then followed by the results of my own investigation of material from the Old Ballast Pit.

Charles Bean's Holditch Lane collection

Charles Bean was active at Holditch Lane between 1932 and 1941, during which time he generated a collection of bifaces numbering between 900 and 1000 artefacts (Green 1988: 177). Bean kept detailed records and in 1942 undertook a study of the collection. Although this was never published, the results have been summarised by Green (1988). Bean's analysis was based on 899 artefacts for which he listed raw material type, rolling, shape and location within the gravel sequence. He defined a total of five sharpness categories which ranged from very sharp to much rolled (Green 1988: 177). My own work on the Old Ballast Pit bifaces indicated that grouping artefacts according to Bean's five subjective rolling categories is extremely difficult. Consequently, these were initially reduced to three categories, sharp, slightly rolled and rolled, and then to just two, sharp and rolled (Table 8.1).

When grouped according to these categories, sharp bifaces comprised 80.9% (n=727) of the collection while rolled artefacts made up just 19.1% (n=172). As with rolling, Bean grouped his collection according to a large number of outline shapes, seventeen in total (Green 1988: 179). My own analysis of the Old Ballast Pit collection suggested that this number of shape classes was unrealistic, and

Suggested rolling categories	Bean's rolling categories:
Sharp	Sharp, Very sharp
Rolled	Slightly rolled, Moderately rolled, Rolled

Table 8.1: suggested rolling categories and those defined by Charles Bean for the Holditch Lane collection

Bean's categories were reduced to the following four basic types (Table 8.2).

Suggested shape categories:	Bean's shape categories:
Ovate	5,6,17
Pointed	1, 3,4,10,16
Ficron	2,9
Other	Other

Table 8.2: suggested shape categories and those defined by Charles Bean for the Holditch Lane collection

Reduced in this way, pointed forms remained dominant at 80% (n=719) of the collection, ovates at 10.9% (n=98), with 'ficrons' and 'others' making up 9.1% (n=82).

When grouped, very similar rates of rolling were noted amongst both 'ovate' and 'pointed' types, while the incidence of rolling increased amongst 'ficrons' and 'other' types (Table 8.3 and Figure 8.1). However in both cases assemblage size was small. The fact that Bean's "other" bifaces could not be fitted into any of his seventeen shape classes suggests they comprise nondescript types, perhaps rough-outs or artefacts other than handaxes.

Biface shape	Sharp (%)	Rolled (%)	Totals (%)
Ovate	81 (82.7)	17 (17.3)	98 (10.9)
Pointed	589 (81.9)	130 (18.1)	719 (80.0)
Ficron	35 (71.4)	14 (28.6)	49 (5.5)
Others	22 (66.7)	11 (33.3)	33 (3.7)
Totals	727 (80.9)	172 (19.1)	899 (100.0)

Table 8.3: rolling and shape categories based on Charles Bean's analysis of the Holditch Lane bifaces (after Green 1988)

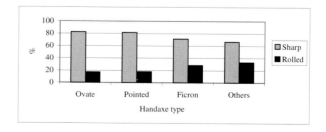

Figure 8.1: rolling and shape for Charles Bean's Holditch Lane biface collection

Summary

Comparison of rolling and shape based on the summaries of Bean's 1942 analysis of the Holditch Lane collection as provided by Green (1988), suggested a significant similarity in the proportions of rolled and fresh artefacts amongst both 'ovate' and 'pointed' types. In effect both appear to have been subjected to similar amounts of post depositional abrasion, suggesting no significant spatial or temporal discontinuity amongst the assemblage. However, amongst 'ficrons' and 'others', there was a slightly greater incidence of rolling, an increase of around ten percent. The significance of this is unclear, the optimistic interpretation being of a slightly greater incidence of rolling due to spatial or temporal separation between abandonment and final burial. The more realistic interpretation however, may be of small sample size amongst 'ficrons' and 'others', or that some other aspect, for instance artefact size or shape determined the extent of rolling. Only further analyses of the whole of the Holditch Lane collection will clarify this point.

The Old Ballast Pit

In the same way as those from Holditch Lane, bifaces from the Old Ballast Pit were investigated in terms of rolling, although in this case the attribute list was increased to six variables. From the collection held by the British Museum, a random sample of 239 bifaces was selected for study. The following analysis made use of 228 chert artefacts, the eleven of flint removed in order to avoid the possible influence of smaller raw materials. As with the previous analysis, the aim was to investigate whether any differences could be identified between the fresh and rolled collections. Bifaces were defined as fresh if they were unrolled or only very slightly abraded, while the remaining pieces were classified as rolled. The sample was divided into fresh and rolled and artefacts described and measured according to the following attributes (Table 8.4).

Attributes
Edge profile
Blank form
Butt working
Proportion worked
Weight
Shape

Table 8.4: attributes listed for the Old Ballast Pit collection

Edge profile

Edge profile provided a measure of the extent to which the edge of the artefact had been straightened. Those straightened through light alternate flaking

over more than 25% of the tool periphery were defined as linear. Twisted pieces included those with obvious 'S' or 'Z' profiles and were all twisted by default. The rest had sinuous edges produced by hard hammer flaking and were described as irregular.

Linear edges were most common amongst fresh pieces (Figure 8.2), whilst amongst rolled bifaces the proportion of irregular pieces increased twofold, equalling that of linear pieces. At the same time there was a slight increase in the proportion of twisted profiles amongst the rolled collection. The greater incidence of irregular profiles amongst the rolled assemblage may suggest an association between rough flaking and a greater incidence of rolling.

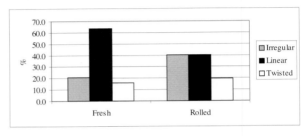

Figure 8.2: edge profile and rolling amongst the Old Ballast Pit collection

Blank form

Blank form provided a simple indication of how the artefact began life, as either a flake or nodule. Flake blanks retained obvious platforms, bulbs or ventral surfaces, while those defined as nodular began life as complete pebbles. Those that could not be definitely attributed to either a flake or nodule blank were classified as unclear.

Blank form was significantly similar amongst both the fresh and rolled sample (Figure 8.3), predominately on flakes.

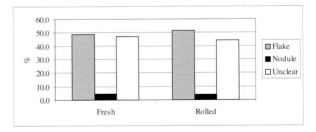

Figure 8.3: blank form and rolling amongst the Old Ballast Pit collection

Butt working

Artefacts were grouped according to the extent of deliberate shaping of the butt. Worked and unworked butts were more common amongst rolled bifaces, while partially worked butts were more common in the fresh collection (Figure 8.4). The greater proportion of unworked butts amongst the rolled collection may suggest some association between

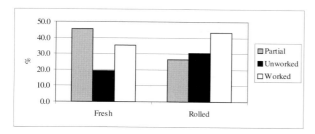

Figure 8.4: butt working and rolling for fresh and rolled bifaces from the Old Ballast Pit collection

rolling and simpler preparation.

Working intensity

Working intensity was expressed as the proportion of the total circumference which was worked. No significant difference was apparent in the cumulative frequency histograms for the fresh and rolled series (Figure 8.5).

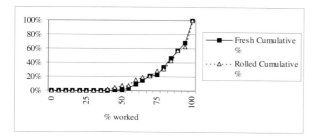

Figure 8.5: working intensity cumulative frequency histogram for fresh and rolled bifaces from the Old Ballast Pit collection

Weight

Weight was used as a simple index of artefact size. No significant difference was noted between the cumulative frequency histograms for the fresh and rolled sample (Figure 8.6), suggesting that bifaces were being abandoned at a similar range of sizes.

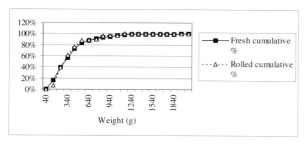

Figure 8.6: weight cumulative frequency histogram for fresh and rolled bifaces from the Old Ballast Pit collection

Shape

Shape analysis was undertaken on the fresh and rolled bifaces following the approach of Roe (1964,

1968). This scheme provides a visual means for presenting complex multidimensional shape data. Pointed and ovate proportions were similar amongst both the fresh and rolled assemblages (Figure 8.7), while none fell within the 'cleaver' group or those with maximum breadth close to the tip. The scattergrams were broadly comparable, however as shown circled, they did suggest the presence of an additional narrow pointed and parallel sided component amongst fresh pointed and ovate types.

Summary

As with the Holditch Lane analysis, associations between rolling and the six descriptive and measured attributes were not particularly significant. In the case of edge profile and butt working however, slightly greater proportions of irregular edges and unworked butts were associated with the rolled collection, perhaps suggesting greater time depth amongst less finely worked artefacts. Blank form, perimeter working and artefact weight showed significant similarity between the fresh and rolled collection. The two assemblages appear to have been made on a similar range of blanks, been similarly worked, and abandoned at broadly the same range of sizes. Shape analysis highlighted the broadly similar nature of the fresh and rolled collections with ovates differing by only about 3% (Figure 8.7), and both classified as type IV indeterminate collections, as did Roe (1968: 11) in his original study of the Old Ballast Pit material. This he suggested reflected the essentially mixed nature of the Old Ballast Pit assemblage. When broken down into the fresh and rolled series, the shape diagrams suggested the presence of additional shapes amongst the fresh collection. Amongst pointed forms these included narrow pointed types including ficrons as well as a series of narrow parallel sided forms. In the case of ovates, additional fresh forms included narrow pointed types and an additional component of circular to oval blunt ended forms. These additional elements amongst the fresh collection do not appear to simply be a result of larger sample size. Rather, they suggest a real difference in terms of the range of biface forms present between the fresh and rolled collection. Clarification of this, along with possible associations between rolling and rougher more expedient artefacts must await further analysis of the Broom collection, and in particular the well documented Holditch Lane collection of Charles Bean.

LONG DISTANCE TRANSPORT OF FLINT AND CHERT

Flint bifaces at Broom were suggested by Hawkes (1943: 51) as indicative of movement between the Hampshire Basin and west country, while chert at Warsash in Hampshire was suggested by Burkitt *et al.*

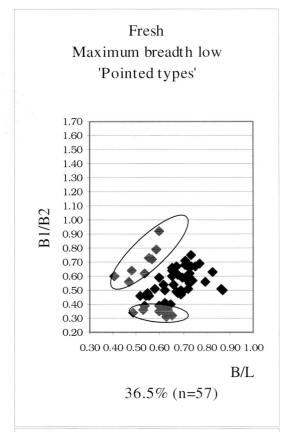

Fresh
Maximum breadth low
'Pointed types'

36.5% (n=57)

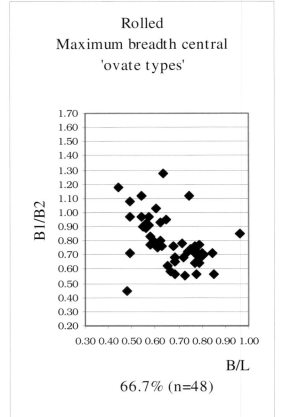

Rolled
Maximum breadth central
'ovate types'

66.7% (n=48)

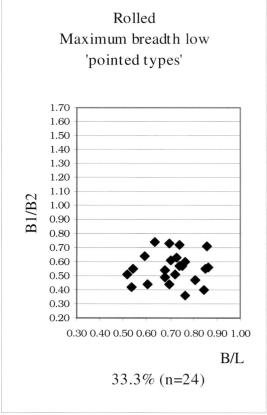

Rolled
Maximum breadth low
'pointed types'

33.3% (n=24)

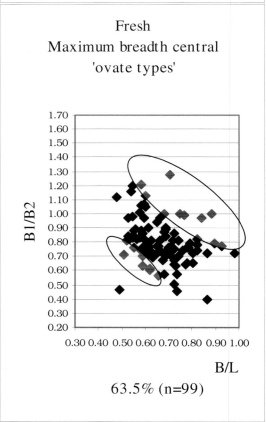

Fresh
Maximum breadth central
'ovate types'

63.5% (n=99)

Figure 8.7: shape diagrams for fresh and rolled bifaces from the Old Ballast pit collection

82

(1939: 39) as indicative of movement in the opposite direction. If correct, this would suggest significant distances were being covered and artefacts curated and transported, something not generally associated with the Acheulian. What then is the evidence for this two way movement of raw materials?

Flint bifaces comprised 4.3% of the Old Ballast Pit sample and 3.1% of Bean's Holditch Lane collection (Green 1988: 17). Hawkes (1943) used this to argue for long distance transport from Hampshire, however as discussed previously, flint does occur naturally within the Axe gravels as a product of erosion of the upper chalk. At Chard Junction just upstream of Broom, naturally occurring flint large enough to produce bifaces was estimated to make up about five percent of the deposit. The presence of locally occurring flint does not rule out longer distance movement, however the principle of least effort suggests that local derivation is more likely.

In the case of chert, a handful of sites have produced artefacts such as at Warsash in Hampshire where two handaxes were recovered in 1939. On the basis of this Burkitt *et al.* (1939: 39) and Hawkes (1943: 51) suggested connections with the West Country and the Axe in particular, the implication of which is of transport of over one hundred kilometres. However, the presence of naturally occurring sources of chert away from the Axe needs to be considered. Derived pebbles can be found along Chesil beach, while greensand with chert is present on the Isle of Wight (Tresise 1961: 334). This is not to say that the Warsash bifaces were made of this material, however these more accessible deposits need to be eliminated before long distance transport can be verified. Evidence exists for shorter distance movements, for instance the biface found in a ploughed field at Pye Corner, Upton Pyne north of Exeter, twenty-six miles west of Broom (Parry 1930). However, when assessing isolated finds it needs to be remembered that much of the material quarried along the Axe valley was destined for the railways, raising the possibility of a much more recent derivation for many stray chert bifaces.

CONCLUSIONS AND THE POTENTIAL FOR FURTHER WORK AT BROOM

The aim of this paper was to briefly summarise the history of collection and research over the past one hundred and fifty or so years along the River Axe, and secondly to act as a pilot study for further work on the Holditch Lane material in particular. As noted by Roe (1968: 11), the true character of the Broom biface assemblages awaits a review of this collection.

Analysis of differences between the fresh and rolled elements of the Old Ballast and Holditch Lane collections was less than conclusive although a number of possible associations were noted. For instance, whist rolling amongst ficrons and other nondescript forms was more common in the Holditch Lane collection, ovate and pointed forms showed a similar incidence of rolling. The Old Ballast Pit collection suggested an association between rolling and irregular edge profiles and unworked butts, which in turn may suggest a chronological association between less refined pieces and a greater incidence of rolling and reworking. Shape analysis on the Old Ballast Pit collection identified an additional narrow pointed element amongst fresh 'ovate' and 'pointed' types, as well as an additional component of fresh broad 'ovates'. Although minimal, these differences do suggest some variation between the fresh and rolled collections, and that a reanalysis of the larger collection of better recorded material from the Holditch Lane pits would be useful.

In terms of the site itself, the presence of both rolled and unrolled artefacts within similar gravel horizons at both the Old Ballast and Holditch Lane pits suggests the possibility of surviving undisturbed deposits. The possible *in situ* clays and silts capping the red beds in which most artefacts were recovered, again suggest the potential for preservation of at least some *in situ* deposits. Broom also represents the most significant north-westerly extent of the Acheulian world, and certainly represents a focus of activity in an area otherwise generally poor in finds. This focusing of activity or visibility probably had a lot to do with the presence of significant quantities of eroding chert, and as such represents the most significant non-flint site in England and much of north-west Europe as well.

This discussion has highlighted the importance of the Broom deposits and has indicated that future investigation needs to be tackled on two fronts. Firstly, Green's (1988) review of the results from Bean's Holditch Lane biface study need to be followed up with a full reanalysis of the collection. Secondly, the exploratory excavation by Shakesby & Stephens (1984) at the Old Ballast Pit needs to be followed up with further exploratory excavations in the *in situ* clays and silts as well as the underlying artefact bearing gravel horizon.

REFERENCES

Ashton, N. & McNabb, J. 1993. Bifaces in perspective. In N. Ashton & A. David (ed's) *Stories in Stone*: 182–191. Lithic Studies Society Occasional Paper No. 4. Lithic Studies Society, London.

Burkitt, M.C., Paterson T.T. & Mogridge, C.J. 1939. The Lower Palaeolithic industries near Warsash, Hampshire. *Proceedings of the Prehistoric Society* V (1): 39–50.

Deacon, H.J. & Deacon, J. 1999. *Human beginnings in South Africa*. Altimira, London.

D'Urban, W.S.M. 1878. Palaeolithic Implements from the valley of the Axe. *The Geological Magazine* 5: 37–38.

Evans, J. 1897, 2nd edition. *The Ancient stone implements, weapons and ornaments, of Great Britain.* Longmans, Green and Co., London and Bombay.

Green, C.P. 1974. Pleistocene gravels of the River Axe in south-western England, and their bearing on the southern limit of glaciation in Britain. *Geological Magazine* 111(3): 213–220.

Green, C.P. 1988. The Palaeolithic site at Broom, Dorset, 1932–41: from the record of C.E. Bean, Esq., F.S.A. *Proceedings of the Geologists' Association* 99: 173–180.

Hawkes, C.F.C. 1943. Two Palaeoliths from Broom, Dorset. *Proceedings of the Prehistoric Society* IX: 48–55.

Reid Moir, J. 1936. Ancient Man in Devon. *Proceedings of the Devon Archaeological Exploration Society* 2: 264–275.

Parry, R.E. 1930. A Palaeolithic implement from Devon. *The Antiquaries Journal* X.

Roe, D.A. 1964. The British Lower and Middle Palaeolithic: Some Problems, Methods of Study and Preliminary Results. *Proceedings of the Prehistoric Society* 30: 245–267.

Roe, D.A. 1968. British Lower and Middle Palaeolithic handaxe groups. *Proceedings of the Prehistoric Society* 34: 1–82.

Salter, A.E. 1906, 1st edition. *The Geology of the Country near Sidmouth and Lyme Regis.* Memoir of the British Geological Survey, Sheet 326 & 340. HMSO, London.

Shakesby, R.A. & Stephens, N. 1984. The Pleistocene gravels of Axe Valley, Devon. *Report of the Transactions of the Devon Association for the Advancement of Science* 116: 77–88.

Stephens, N. 1970. The West Country and Southern Ireland and The Lower Severn Valley. In C.A. Lewis (ed.) *The Glaciations of Wales and Adjoining Regions:* 267–314, 107–124. Longmans, Harlow.

Stephens, N. 1974. Chard area and the Axe Valley sections. In A. Straw (ed.) *Field Handbook for the Quaternary Research Association Easter Meeting 1974*: 46–51. Quaternary Research Association, Exeter.

Stephens, N. 1977. The Axe Valley. In D.N. Mottershead (ed.) *INQUA Congress Guidebook for Excursions. A6 and C6. South West England*: 24–29. Geo Abstracts Ltd., Norwich.

Tresise, G.R. 1961. The Nature and origin of Chert in the Upper Greensand of Wessex. *Proceedings of the Geologists' Association* 72(3): 333–354.

Wessex Archaeology. 1993. *The South West and South of the Thames: the Southern Rivers Palaeolithic Project, Report no. 2, 1992–1993.* Wessex Archaeology, Salisbury.

White, M.J. 1998. On the significance of Acheulean biface variability in Southern Britain. *Proceedings of the Prehistoric Society* 64: 15–44.

Wymer, J. 1999. *The Lower Palaeolithic Occupation of Britain.* Wessex Archaeology, Salisbury.

9. THE LOWER PALAEOLITHIC OF THE SOLENT: 'SITE' FORMATION AND INTERPRETIVE FRAMEWORKS

R.T. Hosfield

ABSTRACT

The Lower Palaeolithic archaeological record of the Solent Basin is dominated by secondary context lithic assemblages, which are frequently associated with river terrace gravel deposits. Interpretation of this archaeology has been hindered by both the spatial and chronological imprecision of the assemblages, and it has subsequently been argued that the behavioural information contained within these 'sites' is extremely limited. This paper adopts a more optimistic stance, presenting an analytical methodology and interpretation of the geological processes by which these 'sites' were formed, with particular emphasis upon artefact transportation and deposition and the chronological affinities of heterogeneous, derived lithic assemblages. Examples are presented for the sites of Wood Green and Dunbridge in the valleys of the Rivers Avon and Test. In conclusion, interpretative frameworks are presented that address research questions relevant to the structure of the archaeological record in the Solent (characterised by regional spatial scales and OIS cycles). Particular attention is paid to repetitive patterns of landscape exploitation and the potential of the data to the study of hominid demography.

INTRODUCTION

The Solent Basin's Lower Palaeolithic archaeological record is dominated by secondary context lithic assemblages (Roe this volume; Wenban-Smith this volume). The archaeology is structurally similar to the majority of 'sites' and find-spots from across southern Britain with the lithic assemblages occurring frequently, although not always, within the deposits of gravels underlying river terraces (Evans 1897; Wymer 1968, 1996, 1999: 21; Roe 1981, 1996). Interpretation of the archaeology is therefore hindered by two major problems (Figure 9.1):

1. Spatial imprecision. After deposition by a hominid agent, solifluction processes and fluvial systems transport the lithic materials downstream.
2. Chronological imprecision. The stone tools are eroded from older gravel deposits at higher elevations, and re-deposited into younger gravels at lower levels.

It has been traditionally argued that the behavioural information contained within river terrace sites and find-spots is extremely limited (e.g. Wymer 1968: 17). Recent syntheses have begun to adopt a more positive view (e.g. Wymer 1999: 21–22), and this paper adopts that approach. It is argued that meaningful information can be extracted from secondary context 'sites', and that the information is relevant to an understanding of hominid behaviour during the Lower Palaeolithic. Underlying these arguments is a central proposition that the information is structurally suited to the analysis of landscapes and the understanding of evolutionary, long-term changes in hominid behaviour.

The interpretation inevitably requires an understanding of the formation of the 'sites' and find-spots. A methodology and related interpretation are therefore presented for two case study 'sites' in the Solent Basin. The methodology and interpretation are primarily concerned with geological processes that

85

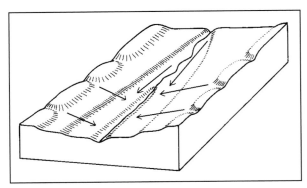

Figure 9.1: spatio-temporal origins of lithic artefacts accumulating within secondary context, river gravel find-spots

may be partially responsible for the formation of secondary context, river gravel 'sites'. Particular

emphasis is placed upon:

1. Cycles of erosion, transportation and deposition that modify lithic artefacts within fluvial systems.
2. The chronological and spatial affinities of heterogeneous, derived lithic assemblages.

Case studies are presented for the 'sites' of Wood Green (Westlake 1889; Crawford 1922; Bury 1923; Bridgland & Harding 1987) and Dunbridge (Dale 1912a, 1918; Bridgland & Harding 1987, 1993) in the Solent Basin (Figure 9.2). Analytical frameworks are explored within the structure of the Palaeolithic archaeological record. These frameworks explore the repetitive patterns of landscape exploitation as expressed through stone tool distribution signatures. The potential of regional lithic data in an examination of hominid demography is also demonstrated.

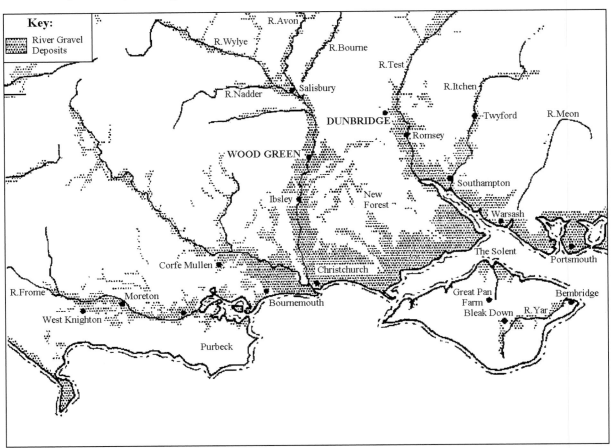

Figure 9.2: Location of Wood Green and Dunbridge in the Solent Basin (after Wymer 1996: Figure 2.4)

THE ARCHAEOLOGICAL RECORD

The 'sites' of Wood Green (Avon valley, SU 172170) and Dunbridge (Test valley, SU 318258) have a long history of archaeological research, stretching back to the end of the 19th and beginning of the 20th centuries.

Wood Green

The 'site' lies on the eastern side of the Avon Valley, three kilometres northeast of the town of Fordingbridge (Figure 9.2). The pit worked Avon Terrace gravel, aggraded to *c.* 56m O.D. (Bridgland & Harding 1987: 45). The first palaeoliths were collected from the pit in the 1870s, with Westlake

(1889: 16–17) listing approximately 24 handaxes and four flakes found by the late 1880s. He observed that many of the artefacts had undergone sub-aerial weathering including fluvial abrasion, before deposition in the gravel (*ibid.* 17). During the 1890s Westlake recorded more than 900 collected artefacts in his personal field notebooks. This figure contrasts markedly with Roe (1968: 117) who listed 409 handaxes and 171 other artefacts (7 roughouts, 1 core, 11 retouched flakes, 143 unretouched flakes, and 9 miscellaneous pieces — Table 9.1). The difference may reflect a fairly catholic definition of Palaeolithic material by Westlake. Subsequent references to Palaeolithic materials from the site were also made by Crawford (1922), Bury (1923) and R.A. Smith (1926).

Artefact type	Wood Green	Dunbridge	Kimbridge
Handaxes	409	953	77
Rough-outs	7	14	3
Cores	1	3	1
Retouched flakes	11	16	2
Unretouched flakes	143	24	3
Miscellaneous	9	8	0
Levallois flakes	0	3	4
Total	580	1021	90

Table 9.1: Palaeolithic artefacts from Wood Green, Dunbridge and Kimbridge (after Roe 1968)

Several authors have classified the Wood Green gravels since the late 19th century. Classifications include the 100 foot terrace (above river level and not ordnance datum) of Westlake (1899, 1903), 1st terrace or Palaeolithic terrace of Reid (1902), Iver terrace (Green 1950), Boyn Hill terrace (Seally 1955), and No. 7 terrace (Kubala 1980; Clark & Green 1987). The final classification originated from the numbered terrace system generated during the British Geological Survey's national resource investigations.

During April 1986 Bridgland & Harding (1987) opened a new section at the site as part of the Nature Conservancy Council's Geological Conservation Review. The single section exposed approximately four metres of bedded, fluvial gravel (Figure 9.3). The gravel was variously fine and coarse, horizontally and cross-stratified, matrix supported and open framework (*ibid.* 46). Bedrock of Bagshot Beds sand lay at just above 51m O.D. The exposed bedrock surface revealed small-scale relief in the form of possible scour features with an amplitude of 23cm. Bridgland & Harding suggested that they might be comparable to features in the London Clay bedrock beneath fluvial gravel at Stoke Newington (*ibid.* 46).

Bridgland & Harding recovered a small rolled, *in situ*, handaxe (*ibid.* Figure 2) and two rolled, unstratified flakes. Preliminary calculations suggested that Wood Green was a richer site for palaeoliths than Dunbridge in terms of artefacts found per volume of gravel exploited.

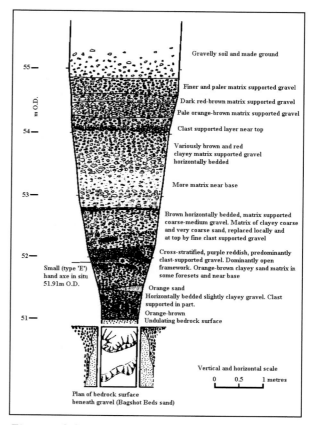

Figure 9.3: Section at Wood Green (after Bridgland & Harding 1987: Figure 2)

Dunbridge

The Dunbridge gravel pits lie to the west of the river Test, immediately below its confluence with the tributary river Dun (Figure 9.2). The gravel deposit rises away from the river, reaching over 40m O.D. The gravel pits have predominantly exploited the lower deposits adjacent to the river, cutting into the northern edge of the gravel and facing the river Dun. The workings have exposed the largest collection of Palaeolithic artefacts from a single locality in Hampshire, and there are further low-level pits on the eastern edge of the gravel deposit at Kimbridge (Bridgland & Harding 1987: 50).

The gravels at Dunbridge were extensively worked during the first quarter of the 20th century. Collections were made by William Dale (1912a, 1918), a local Southampton-based antiquarian, and there are also references to the site made by Sturge (1912) and R.A. Smith (1926). Roe (1968: 96) listed 1021 artefacts, including 953 handaxes (93.3%). The remainder of the assemblage includes 14 roughouts, 3 cores, 16 retouched flakes, 24 unretouched flakes, 8 miscellaneous pieces, and 3 Levallois flakes (Table 9.1). A watching brief was undertaken during the 1990s at the Kimbridge Farm pit (adjacent to the old Dunbridge 'site'), by Phil Harding of Wessex Archaeology. This work produced a far lower ratio of handaxes to other collected artefacts. The composition of Roe's assemblage undoubtedly reflects selective collection during the early part of the 20th century. It is unfortunately impossible to reconstruct the proportions of artefact types for the gravels extracted during that period. Nonetheless the recent watching brief suggests that large quantities of non-bifacial material may have been ignored. Roe (*ibid.* 101) also lists 90 artefacts from the Kimbridge pits, including 77 handaxes (Table 9.1).

Dale (1912a) described up to 7m of gravel at Dunbridge, overlying an irregular surface cut into clays and sands of the Woolwich and Reading Beds (Figure 9.4). Dale also suggested that palaeoliths with different states of preservation had originated from different stratigraphic levels in the gravel. It was proposed that the sharp, white implements from the upper deposit where of a 'later character' than those from the lower beds (Dale 1918). The sub-division of the gravel deposit was based on colour: a lower dark red gravel, a middle yellow-brown gravel and an upper white gravel. Dale subsequently modified this interpretation and suggested that the gravel of two periods was present. In this later view, an upper, paler deposit was separated from a lower, darker aggradation by an iron pan horizon. Bridgland & Harding (1987: 50) suggest that the middle and lower units of Dale's tripartite division had been combined into the lower, darker aggradation of the later interpretation. Dale's (1912a, 1918) observations suggested the possibility that different Lower Palaeolithic industries existed in stratigraphic superposition at Dunbridge. Following these claims Roe (1981) examined the range of material from the site and was able to identify the white material described by Dale.

Dale (1912b) recognised separate 100 and 150 feet gravels at Dunbridge and Kimbridge. Although geological mapping indicated a single spread of gravel, the geological memoir (White 1912) recognised two levels. White described an upper Belbins stage (21m above river level) and a lower Mottisfont stage (12m above the river), both yielding Palaeolithic materials. White assigned the Dunbridge gravel to the Belbins stage and the Kimbridge gravel to the Mottisfont stage. He also disputed Dale's (1912a, 1912b) claim that the Dunbridge deposits might have a sub-glacial origin.

Bridgland & Harding (1987: 51) excavated three sections at the old Dunbridge workings in 1986. They noted that the deposits were of a brown, ferruginously stained appearance and were unable to subdivide the gravel into upper white and lower darker units. The single iron pan horizon could also not be identified. White patinated flints were recorded in the upper layers of sections 2 and 3, but they were also observed from lower down in section 3.

In 1991, four sections were recorded at the Kimbridge Farm 'site' (Bridgland & Harding 1993). A distinction was drawn between lower, well-bedded,

generally unbleached gravel, and an upper, poorly bedded or unbedded, generally bleached gravel. The bleached and unbleached gravels were typically separated by a persistent iron / manganese pan, although the pan did not necessarily coincide with the top of the well-bedded gravel. This distinction, not apparent in the 1986 sections, may support Dale's (1912a, 1918) stratigraphic claims (Bridgland & Harding 1993: 8–9).

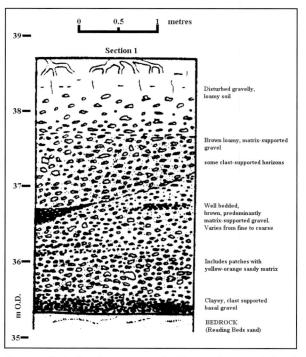

Figure 9.4: Section at Dunbridge (after Bridgland & Harding 1987: Figure 5)

INTERPRETATION

There has been a long-standing typological approach applied to the interpretation of these types of Lower Palaeolithic sites (e.g. Roe 1968, 1981). For example, the site of Dunbridge has been discussed in terms of the predominance of pointed handaxes, mostly of the Group II manner (Roe 1981: 206). Similarly, the occurrence of 'many ovates' is highlighted at the Wood Green findspot (*ibid.* p. 210). With respect to the origins of the material, Wessex Archaeology (1993) and Wymer (1999) reflect a prevailing viewpoint. It is argued that where dense concentrations of artefacts occur, the lithics have not been transported far from their point of discard. Subsequent re-working of the gravel would further disperse the lithics, both horizontally and vertically. Following this argument, it should be possible to identify 'dense concentration findspots' as evidence for significant local 'sites' and activities. Momentarily ignoring the question of what makes a 'site' significant, the spatial and chronological implications of this approach are twofold:

1. The artefacts were discarded relatively close to the findspot, probably within a few hundred metres upstream. Longer transport distances would have reduced the concentration of material through size sorting and the differential effects of fluvial sub-systems.
2. The artefacts were discarded, transported and deposited within a single glacial-interglacial cycle. Subsequent re-working through rejuvenation events would have dispersed the artefact concentration.

Yet whatever the spatio-temporal structure of these 'sites' and findspots, the question of how to interpret them remains. The archaeology is evidence of sub-regional, if not immediately local, occupation, but it is very difficult to estimate the duration of that occupation. Questions concerning how many hominids were present and how many individual occupation events are represented, remain similarly inaccessible (Wymer 1999: 193). The massive changes undergone by landscapes and environments since the Middle Pleistocene make it difficult to identify the specific attractions of local environments such as those surrounding Wood Green and

Dunbridge (cf. Wymer 1999: 113). It is possible to discuss those attractions at an abstract level, highlighting raw material availability, animal migration routes, and other resource issues. But if such abstractions are the limitations of our answers, then might this be an example of asking the wrong questions (Gamble 1996: 64)?

This paper proposes alternative questions, focusing upon two themes:

1. The presence or absence of spatial structure in the regional archaeological record of the British Lower Palaeolithic.
2. The demographic implications of the artefact assemblages.

Space and Structure

The first theme seeks to build upon existing models of land use and habitat exploitation during the Early and Middle Pleistocene (e.g. Potts 1991: Figure 6). It attempts to bridge the temporal contrast between models of hominid behaviour and the archaeological record. Models including Isaac's (1980) home base, Binford's (1984) routed foraging and Pott's (1988) stone cache interpretations have tended to view hominid behaviour and the resultant material deposits

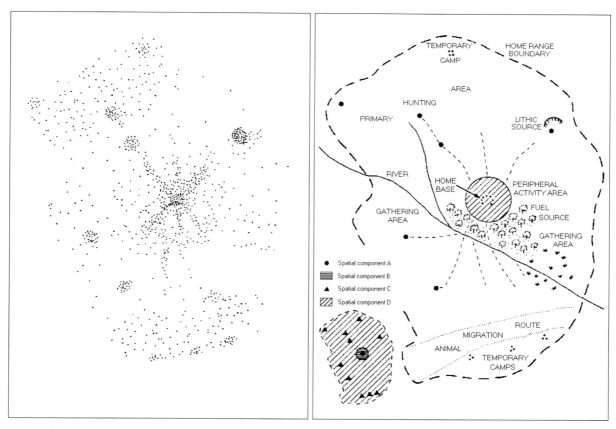

Figure 9.5: model of regional archaeological structure (after Foley 1981: Figure 1)

over ecological time (cf. Potts 1991: 168). This is equally true of Foley's (1981) model of regional archaeological structure (Figure 9.5).

Stern (1993, 1994) has already demonstrated for the east African Early Pleistocene archaeological record that there is a mismatch between the available interpretive models and the structure of the data. This mismatch is also apparent when the British Lower Palaeolithic evidence is highlighted. The relationship between climatic cycles and terrace formation produces gravel deposits with a minimum chronological duration of *c.* 70–100,000 years (Bridgland 1994). The behavioural information contained within depositional units of that duration would inevitably be subject to time averaging and blurring. At local scales the lithic materials have been removed from their contexts of hominid deposition by fluvial processes. There are few, if any, current interpretive models suitable for the study of this type of chronologically coarse archaeological deposit.

The distribution of lithic materials across Wales and the south of England support a regional search for structure in the archaeological record. This operates at a national level, where Gamble (1987) and Wymer (1968) have observed the concentration of Lower Palaeolithic artefacts along the Thames, East Anglian and Solent River systems. But it also operates at the regional landscape level, where the distribution of lithics along river valley systems can be investigated for spatial structuring. Contrasting with the ecological structuring of artefacts suggested by Foley (1981: Figure 1), a starting hypothesis proposes that the spatial distribution of artefacts should be 'time averaged'. The rejection or acceptance of such a hypothesis inevitably raises a series of secondary questions.

Hominid Demography

The second theme examines artefact assemblages through the study of hominid demography. The fluvial gravel chronology provides an evolutionary view of changes in hominid colonisation strategies, measured through demographic variation. This perspective is in marked contrast to the ecological view of population sizes provided by on-site evidence (Wymer 1999). The approach utilises the selective collection of handaxes during the last century and a half, an archaeological practice that has often been seen as problematic to modern research (Roe 1981). Demographic interpretations are based upon modelled rates of handaxe discard, exploring the variables of artefact function, use and durability. The demographic models' assessments of population density and occupational continuity have significant implications for future studies of hominid foraging strategies, survival capabilities, and land-use exploitation.

These two interpretive themes emphasise the importance of two methodological stages in the examination of the British data:

1. Assessing the fragmentary discovery, collection and publication of the Lower Palaeolithic archaeological record. A GIS-based spatial modelling application was developed to quantify the unsystematic sampling strategies that have been applied to the British Palaeolithic data (Hosfield 1999a, 1999b: chap. 3–4, in press). The model represents the processes by which the Lower Palaeolithic record of Britain has been discovered — aggregates extraction, urbanisation and infrastructure development, and antiquarian fieldwork. The recorded sample is statistically quantified as a percentage of the total (and unknown) material sample. The modelling therefore provides the base for subsequent investigations of the lithic data.
2. Assessing available geological and experimental archaeological evidence to evaluate the spatial origins of secondary context lithic assemblages:
   - That all secondary context, river gravel material is locally derived from within a few hundred metres upstream.
   - Or that spatial modelling of the horizontal and vertical derivation of the transported materials is an achievable goal.

ASSEMBLAGE ORIGINS

The range of abrasion states occurring on lithic material from Lower Palaeolithic findspots in the Solent Basin indicates that at least some of the material has probably been transported significant distances by rivers in spate. Microscopic examination of handaxe abrasion data and comparison with experimental materials (Harding *et al.* 1987) and previous studies (Shackley 1974) suggested that some artefacts have been transported over several kilometres. These extensive transportation distances have been recorded both for stray finds (the product of homogeneous assemblage dispersal) and materials from densely concentrated assemblages such as Dunbridge and Wood Green.

The Wood Green and Dunbridge assemblages contain material abraded to a variety of different states (Figure 9.6). This suggests that the materials have been transported both long and short distances. Yet this transportation evidence is at odds with the dense concentrations of artefacts at the two sites. Wessex Archaeology (1993) argue that transportation of material over long distances will result in the dispersal of a homogeneous assemblage, through size sorting and the differential behaviour of fluvial sub-systems.

A potential solution to the dichotomy lies in the geological setting of these sites. Of particular significance are the fluvial bedrocks and their impact upon river rejuvenation behaviour and terrace preservation conditions. Bridgland (1985) and Allen & Gibbard (1993) have discussed the phenomena, although not in this context.

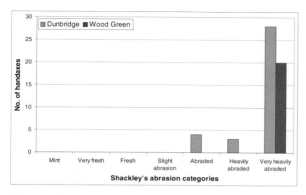

Figure 9.6: abrasion of handaxe samples from Wood Green and Dunbridge

Allen & Gibbard (*ibid.* 520–521) observed the unidirectional migration of the Solent River and its major tributaries, including the Test and the Avon. The Solent River and the lower reaches of its tributaries flowed predominantly over Tertiary clays and sands. During downcutting episodes the rivers moved laterally, incising into the bedrock rather than the recently deposited gravel aggradations (Figure 9.7). Allen & Gibbard suggested that the initial direction of migration would be determined by factors including local hydrology, slope of land, and topographical aspect.

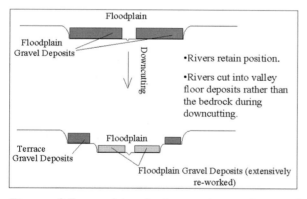

Figure 9.7: model of river rejuvenation and terrace preservation on Tertiary bedrock

Upstream of Dorchester where the river Frome flowed over chalk, the valley was narrow, with steep sides. This pattern is repeated in the Test and Avon rivers where the channels flow over chalk bedrock in their upper reaches. Allen & Gibbard argued that the rivers would retain their positions during downcutting events, as it was easier to erode former gravel accumulations than cut a wider valley in the chalk (Figure 9.8). The resultant valleys, lacking long terrace sequences, have been observed by Bridgland (1985: 29–30) for other chalk bedrock rivers in southern England.

The consequence of these processes is repeated cycles of erosion and deposition in chalk bedrock rivers. These cycles will occur both between and during glacial-interglacial cycles, at micro (individual flooding) and macro (river rejuvenation) scales (Figure 9.9 & Bridgland this volume). Materials are therefore deposited in terrace gravels through the processes of erosion and aggradation. The artefact-bearing gravels are successively reworked during subsequent rejuvenation of the river, and transported further down the chalk stream.

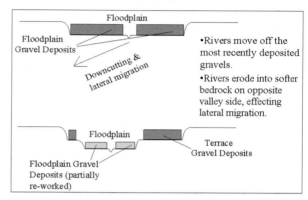

Figure 9.8: model of river rejuvenation and terrace preservation on Chalk bedrock

In the Solent Basin, the Test and Avon rivers flow from the chalk bedrock onto the tertiary sands and clays (Figure 9.10). This geological change results in a transformation in the river's regime of erosion and deposition. The artefact-bearing gravels undergo a single cycle of transportation and deposition in the tertiary bedrock rivers, as a result of the channel's lateral incision. Lithic materials are deposited in river gravels, which are subsequently preserved during the next downcutting event as a result of the river's lateral migration and preferential erosion of the bedrock (Figure 9.7).

The archaeology of the Solent Basin supports this geological model. The findspots of Dunbridge, Wood Green and Corfe Mullen (all producing at least 100 handaxes) are located immediately downstream of the transition from chalk to tertiary bedrock (Figure 9.10). It is not argued that this alternative model of site formation is applicable to all Lower Palaeolithic findspots with dense concentrations of lithics. It does appear to be applicable in this situation, with the artefact abrasion data also indicating a combination of materials transported long distances and locally derived assemblages (following Wessex Archaeology 1993). It should be apparent however that this 'site' formation theory will influence spatial models of artefact distribution and related studies of land use and demography.

The geological model partially rejects the claim that all the material in findspots with dense artefact concentrations has been locally derived. Such models addressing the vertical and horizontal derivation of

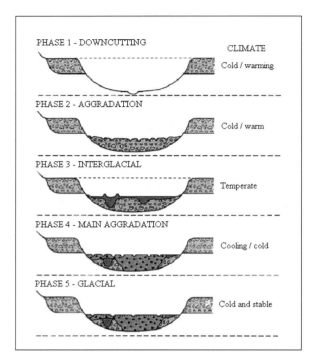

Figure 9.9: Bridgland's 5-phase cyclical climatic model of river terrace formation (after Bridgland 1995: Figure 5)

artefacts must therefore underpin a study of the spatial distributions of Lower Palaeolithic stone tools.

Initial abrasion experiments in 1997 suggested provisional rates of artefact abrasion (Hosfield 1999: chap. 6), although this work was inevitably a simplification of a highly complex process. Abrasion models were developed to 'track' the materials from their findspots to 'zones of hominid discard' upstream, representing the findspots' 'artefact catchment areas' (*ibid.* chap. 6–7). The spatial distribution of artefacts from a single drainage catchment are plotted for the river Test in Figure 9.11, with the river valley represented as 1km wide 'zones of hominid discard' from source to mouth. The temporal distribution of artefacts was modelled according to the bedrock type, following the modern remnants of the river valley's terrace sequence (*ibid.* chap. 6). These data were utilised to approximate the role of vertical artefact derivation.

STRUCTURE AND DEMOGRAPHY

These models have been developed to support an investigation of spatial patterning in the Lower Palaeolithic. The example presented indicates a statistically non-uniform distribution of artefacts along the river Test valley. Figure 9.11 indicates favoured 'zones of hominid discard' between the river's source and mouth. The geological abrasion models were intended to remove the impact of fluvial processes upon the artefact distributions, although it is

likely that there are still background traces evident. It is suggested that the non-continuous, time-averaged distribution of artefacts indicate the impact of Pleistocene habitat and 'cultural' variables upon the hominid behaviours that resulted in handaxe discard. These variables might include the distribution of raw materials and hominid lithic economy, although flint is ubiquitous in the Solent Basin. Distributions of plant and animal foods, the routing of animal migrations, and hominids' perception and interaction with their landscapes through paths and tracks (Gamble 1999: chap. 3–4) are all likely to have been additional factors.

The important issues when interpreting these modelled distributions are not the specific causes of the patterns however, as these are impractical to detect at the spatial and temporal scales of the data. What the distributions do suggest is that hominid behaviour is spatially structured, with handaxe discard activities focused upon local habitats or ecological niches. In other words, the hominids are selectively exploiting the river valley environment. They are not simply wandering from meal to meal as Pleistocene walking stomachs.

Figure 9.12 indicates spatial shifts in the distribution of artefacts over time, between individual glacial-interglacial cycles. These patterns might reflect habitat change, particularly relevant in light of the cycling coastal / non-coastal status of the Solent Basin in response to Pleistocene sea-level variation. Local resource exhaustion is another potential cause of the spatial variation. But it is notable that these changes occur over geological rather than ecological time (Figure 9.12 documents a change in time-averaged patterns that are deposited during *c.* 70–100,000 year units). Do the changing distributions reflect hominid attachment to and exploitation of specific locales during individual occupation episodes? Might these 'landscape memories' be broken by long periods of abandonment?

There is certainly evidence for long abandonment in the demographic models generated from the Solent Basin data. The demographic models compared the observed numbers of recorded handaxes with predicted totals of discarded artefacts. The observed handaxe totals are mathematically modelled to take account of the selective recovery of Palaeolithic materials and the partial exposure of artefact-bearing Pleistocene deposits (Hosfield 1999: chap. 3–4). The predicted handaxe totals were generated from the following assumptions:

- A 25–30 person hominid group, following Foley (1981).

- Handaxes were utilised for butchery, following Jones (1980), Schick & Toth (1993) and White (1996).

- One butchery event per week, following Spiess (1979).

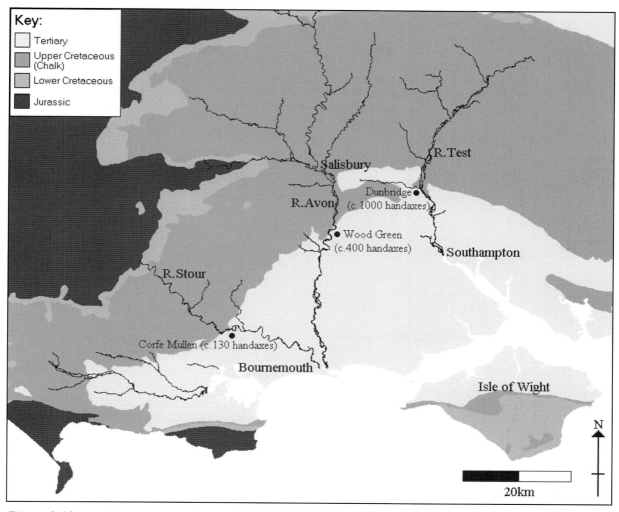

Figure 9.10: pre-Quaternary geology of the Solent Basin and three Lower Palaeolithic find-spots

- One handaxe discarded per 10 butchery events, following Pitts & Roberts (1997) and Pope (pers. comm.).

- Home range size of *c.* 3400km², following Féblot -Augustins (1997).

- Occupation during the open tundra phase (*c.* 56% of the period 500–128,000 years BP), following Stringer & Gamble (1993).

A comparison was made of the resultant predicted total (317 handaxes per km²) against the observed totals for the period 500–128kyr (the open tundra phase). The data suggested either highly intermittent occupation (3.5% of the open tundra phase — *c.* 7,000 years) with a relatively high population density (0.007 individuals per km²); or continuous open phase occupation (*c.* 208,000 years) with very low population density (e.g. 0.00025 individual per km²). These interpretations of the demographic data reflect the two extreme points on a continuum of high density / non-continuous occupation versus low density / continuous occupation (Figure 9.13). The current research climate would favour the former interpretation, since the latter view requires long-term

hominid survival at very low densities. Extrapolation of these data to meet Wobst's (1974) mating network of 175–500 individuals would require an area of 700,000–2,000,000km² (*c.* 835–1415 sq. km). These figures sit uncomfortably with the view of Middle Pleistocene hominid society as locally orientated (Stringer & Gamble 1993; Gamble 1999).

The high density / non-continuous occupation interpretation potentially supports the artefact distribution models discussed above. A model of extremely short-lived occupations (perhaps just a few generations) separated by millennia of abandonment is in keeping with non-continuous, time-averaged distributions and significant spatial variation between glacial-interglacial cycles. Continuous, low density occupations might be expected to generate uniform, time-averaged artefact distributions. By contrast, local extinction and long periods of abandonment would result in loss of local knowledge — each new colonisation episode would be a walk into the unknown.

The demographic model is conditioned by a series of variables, whose modification inevitably alters the output. Nonetheless, the above example illustrates the

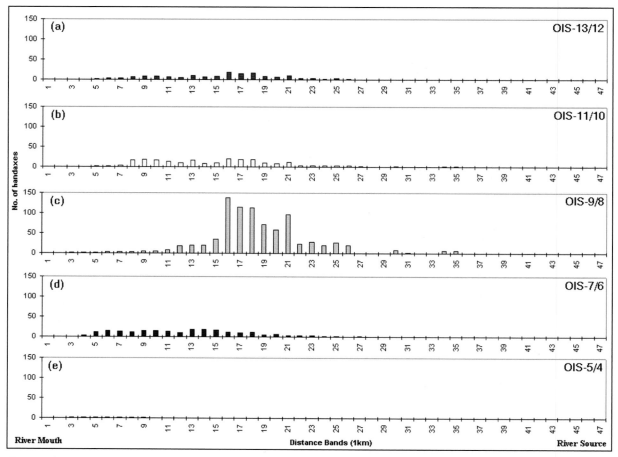

Figure 9.11: modelled distribution of handaxes along the River Test valley

scale of the British data and the potential magnitude (or lack of it) of hominid occupation at high latitudes during the Middle Pleistocene.

CONCLUSIONS

The exploratory nature and model-dependency of this research is no doubt apparent. Its intention is to demonstrate the value of secondary context data, predominant not just in the Solent Basin but also throughout the majority of the British Lower Palaeolithic record. The structure of the data (70,000 year temporal units and regional spatial distributions) conditions the questions that may be asked, but it does not limit the potential of the evidence. Future research will continue to explore the impact of the models and the magnitude of regional data from other areas of Britain and Europe.

On-site evidence enables detailed exploration of vital questions including subsistence strategies, raw material use and economy, and lithic technology. But only at regional and glacial-interglacial scales is it possible to view the evolutionary consequences of those behaviours and their changes over time. Regional approaches to land use and demography can provide a vital perspective to an improved understanding of the Palaeolithic.

ACKNOWLEDGEMENTS

Thank you to English Heritage for their permission to work with the Southern Rivers Palaeolithic Project data, and to Wessex Archaeology for providing digital copies of the relevant information. Thanks also to Professor Clive Gamble and Dr David Wheatley for their extensive support during the completion of the doctoral thesis whose research is partly presented in this paper. The paper was written and presented while the author was undertaking a British Academy-funded Postdoctoral Research Fellowship.

REFERENCES

Allen, L.G. & Gibbard, P.L. 1993. Pleistocene evolution of the Solent River of southern England. *Quaternary Science Review* 12: 503–528.

Binford, L.R. 1984. *Faunal Remains from Klasies River Mouth*. Academic Press, Orlando.

Bridgland, D.R. 1985. Uniclinal shifting: A speculative reappraisal based on terrace distribution in the London Basin. *Quaternary Newsletter* 47: 26–33.

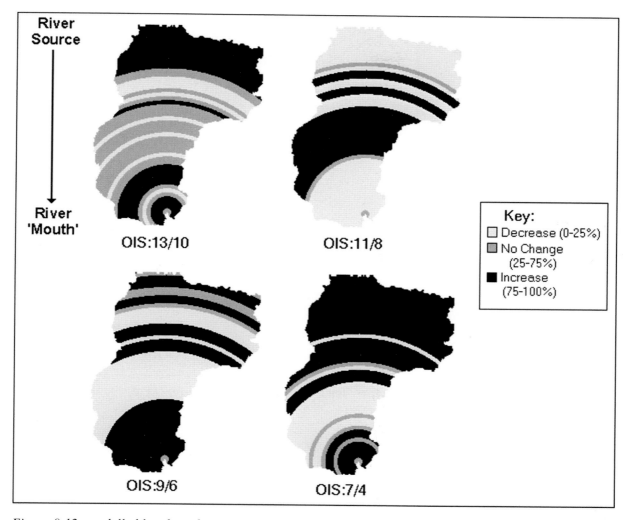

Figure 9.12: modelled handaxe densities in the River Test catchment by glacial–interglacial cycle; density categories (decrease; no change; increase) calculated from previous 3-OIS span plot

Bridgland, D.R. & Harding, P.A. 1987. Palaeolithic sites in tributary valleys of the Solent River. In K.E. Barber (ed.) Wessex and the Isle of Wight: Field Guide: 45–58. Quaternary Research Association, Cambridge.

Bridgland, D.R. & Harding, P.A. 1993. Preliminary Observations at the Kimbridge Farm Quarry, Dunbridge, Hampshire: Early Results of a Watching Brief. *Quaternary Newsletter* 69: 1–9.

Bury, H. 1923. Some aspects of the Hampshire Plateau Gravels. *Proceedings of the Prehistoric Society of East Anglia* 4(1): 15–41.

Clarke, M.R. & Green, C.P. 1987. The Pleistocene terraces of the Bournemouth-Fordingbridge area. In K.E. Barber (ed.) *Wessex and the Isle of Wight: Field Guide:* 58–64. Quaternary Research Association, Cambridge.

Crawford, O.G.S., Ellaway, J.R. & Willis, G.W. 1922. The Antiquity of Man in Hampshire. *Papers and Proceedings of the Hampshire Field Club and Archaeological Society* 9(2): 173–188.

Dale, W. 1912a. On the Implement-bearing gravel beds of the lower valley of the Test. *Proceedings of the Society of Antiquaries* 24: 108–116.

Dale, W. 1912b. Discussion. In Hull, E. On the Interglacial gravel beds of the Isle of Wight and the South of England, and the conditions of their formation

(Abstract). *Quarterly Journal of the Geological Society of London* 68: 21–22.

Dale, W. 1918. Report as Local Secretary for Hampshire. *Proceedings of the Society of Antiquaries* 30: 20–32.

Evans, J. 1897, 2nd edition. *The Ancient Stone Implements, Weapons and Ornaments, of Great Britain.* Longmans, Green, and Co., London.

Féblot-Augustins, J. 1997. *La circulation des matières premières au Paléolithique.* Études et Recherches Archéologiques de l'Université de Liege No. 75. ERAUL, Liege.

Foley, R. 1981. A model of regional archaeological structure. *Proceedings of the Prehistoric Society* 47: 1–17.

Gamble, C.S. 1987. Man the Shoveler: Alternative models for Middle Pleistocene colonization and occupation in northern latitudes. In O. Soffer (ed.) *The Pleistocene Old World. Regional Perspectives:* 81–98. Plenum Press, New York.

Gamble, C.S. 1996. Hominid Behaviour in the Middle Pleistocene: an English Perspective. In C.S. Gamble & A.J. Lawson (ed's) *The English Palaeolithic Reviewed:* 61–71. Wessex Archaeology Ltd, Salisbury.

Gamble, C.S. 1999. *The Palaeolithic Societies of Europe.* Cambridge University Press, Cambridge.

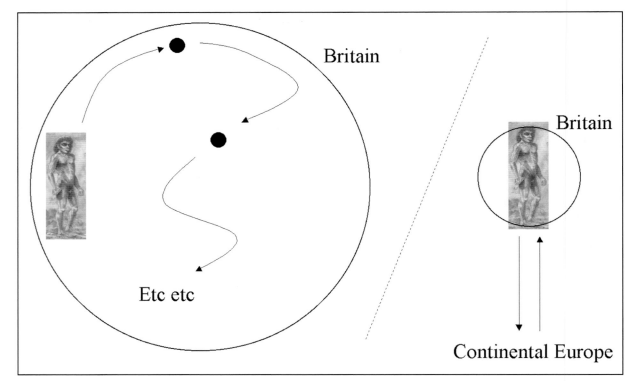

Figure 9.13: models of Middle Pleistocene hominid occupation of the Solent Basin; lower density, continuous occupation (left) versus higher density, sporadic occupation (right)

Green, J.F.N. 1950. A tour of the terraces of the Avon and Stour, *Proceedings of the Bournemouth Natural Science Society* 39: 52–59.

Harding, P., Gibbard, P.L., Lewin J., Macklin, M.G. & Moss, E.H. 1987. The transport and abrasion of flint handaxes in a gravel-bed river. In G. de G. Sieveking & M.H. Newcomer (ed's) *The Human Uses of Flint and Chert: Proceedings of the Fourth International Flint Symposium Held at Brighton Polytechnic, Oct-15 April 1983:* 115–126. Cambridge University Press, Cambridge.

Hosfield, R.T. 1999a. Quantifying the British Palaeolithic: Unsystematic Traditions. In J.A. Barceló, I. Briz & A. Vila (ed's) *New Techniques for Old Times. CAA98. Computer Applications and Quantitative Methods in Archaeology*: 245–253. BAR International Series 757. Archaeopress, Oxford.

Hosfield, R.T. 1999b. *The Palaeolithic of the Hampshire Basin: a regional model of hominid behaviour during the Middle Pleistocene.* BAR British Series 286. Archaeopress, Oxford.

Hosfield, R.T. In press. Quantifying the British Palaeolithic: Regional Data and Hominid Adaptations. In D.W. Wheatley, G.P. Earl & S. Poppy (ed's) *Contemporary themes in Archaeological Computing.* Oxbow Books, Oxford.

Isaac, G.L. 1980. Casting the Net Wide: A Review of Archaeological Evidence for Early Hominid Land-Use and Ecological Relations. In L.K. Königsson (ed.) *Current Argument on Early Man*: 226–251. Pergamon Press, Oxford.

Jones, P.R. 1980. Experimental butchery with modern stone tools and its relevance for Palaeolithic archaeology. *World Archaeology* 12(2): 153–165.

Kubala, A. 1980. *The sand and gravel resources of the country north of Bournemouth, Dorset. Description of parts of 1:25,000 sheets SU 00, 10, 20, SZ 09, 19 and 29.* Mineral Assessment Report 51, Institute of Geological Sciences. HMSO, London.

Pitts, M. & Roberts, M.B. 1997. *Fairweather Eden.* Century Books Limited, London.

Potts, R.B. 1988. *Early Hominid Activities at Olduvai.* Aldine, New York.

Potts, R.B. 1991. Why the Oldowan? Plio-Pleistocene Toolmaking and the Transport of Resources. *Journal of Anthropological Research* 47: 153–176.

Reid, C. 1902. *The Geology of the Country around Ringwood.* Memoir of the British Geological Survey, Sheet 314. HMSO, London.

Roe, D.A. 1968. *Gazetteer for British Lower and Middle Palaeolithic Sites.* Council for British Archaeology, London.

Roe, D.A. 1981. *The Lower and Middle Palaeolithic Periods in Britain.* Routledge and Kegan Paul Ltd, London.

Roe, D.A. 1996. Artefact Distributions and the British Earlier Palaeolithic. In C.S. Gamble & A.J. Lawson (ed's) *The English Palaeolithic Reviewed*: 1–6. Wessex Archaeology Ltd, Salisbury.

Schick, K.D. & Toth, N. 1993. *Making Silent Stones Speak.* Simon and Schuster, New York.

Seally, K.R. 1955. The terraces of the Salisbury Avon. *Geographical Journal* 121: 350–356.

Shackley, M.L. 1974. Stream abrasion of flint implements. *Nature* 248: 501–502.

Smith, R.A. 1926, 3rd edition. *Guide to Antiquities of the Stone Age in the Department of the British and Medieval Antiquities.* British Museum, London.

Spiess, A.E. 1979. *Reindeer and Caribou Hunters: An Archaeological Study.* Academic Press, London.

Stern, N. 1993. The Structure of the Lower Pleistocene Archaeological Record. *Current Anthropology* 34(3): 201–224.

Stern, N. 1994. The implications of time-averaging for reconstructing the land-use patterns of early tool-using hominids. *Journal of Human Evolution* 27(1–3): 89–105.

Stringer, C. & Gamble C.S. 1993. *In search of the Neanderthals: solving the puzzle of human origins.* Thames and Hudson, London.

Sturge, W.A. 1912. The patina of flint implements. *Proceedings of the Prehistoric Society of East Anglia* 1: 140–157.

Westlake, E. 1989. *Outlines of the Geology of Fordingbridge and Neighbourhood.* Titus Mitchell, Fordingbridge.

Westlake, E. 1903. *Note on Recent Discoveries of Palaeolithic and Eolithic Implements in the Valley of the Avon.* W.H. King and Son, Fordingbridge.

White, H.J.O. 1912. *The Geology of the Country around Winchester and Stockbridge.* Memoir of the British Geological Survey, Sheet 299. HMSO, London.

White, M.J. 1996. *Biface Variability and Human Behaviour in the Earlier Palaeolithic: A Study from south-eastern England.* Unpublished Ph.D. Thesis, University of Cambridge.

Wobst, H.M. 1974. Boundary conditions for Palaeolithic social systems: a simulation approach. *American Antiquity* 39: 147–178.

Wessex Archaeology. 1993. *The Southern Rivers Palaeolithic Project: Report No. 1, 1991–1992. The Upper Thames Valley, the Kennet Valley and the Upper Solent Drainage System.* Wessex Archaeology, Salisbury.

Wymer, J.J. 1968. *Lower Palaeolithic Archaeology in Britain as represented by the Thames Valley.* John Baker, London.

Wymer, J.J. 1996. The English Rivers Palaeolithic Survey. In C.S. Gamble & A.J. Lawson (ed's) *The English Palaeolithic Reviewed*: 7–22. Wessex Archaeology Ltd., Salisbury.

Wymer, J.J. 1999. *The Lower Palaeolithic Occupation of Britain.* Trust for Wessex Archaeology Ltd, Salisbury.

10. PROSPECTING THE PALAEOLITHIC: STRATEGIES FOR THE ARCHAEOLOGICAL INVESTIGATION OF MIDDLE PLEISTOCENE DEPOSITS IN SOUTHERN ENGLAND

K. Wilkinson

ABSTRACT

Current find-spot data from the southern English Palaeolithic are reviewed. These are mostly associated with Middle Pleistocene gravel terraces and are mainly the products of aggregate extraction and antiquarian exploration in the later 19th and early 20th centuries. It is argued that current knowledge is therefore largely the result of practice over which today's archaeologists have no control, and therefore that the data is not ideal for present needs. In order to remedy the situation a programme of prospection for new sites is suggested. This could advantageously happen as part of the planning process, focussing particularly on the in situ *sites which are so rare in the English Lower Palaeolithic record. Riverine and coastal depositional environments are suggested as being especially relevant for study as both contain fine grained deposits likely to contain well preserved* in situ *remains. Strategies for investigation of such 'marker beds' are given, based on bore-hole survey, geophysics, watching briefs and field evaluation.*

INTRODUCTION

The year 2000 marks the 200th anniversary of John Frere's publication of a collection of palaeoliths recovered from a brickpit at Hoxne, Suffolk in 1797 (Frere 1800), an event that marked the beginning of British Palaeolithic research. In the two centuries that have followed a great deal has changed; investigative techniques have immeasurably improved (e.g. Roberts 1999b), (reasonably) secure Pleistocene chronologies have been developed (e.g. Bowen 1999) and interpretive frameworks established (e.g. Gamble 1986, 1996, 1999). Nevertheless much of the Palaeolithic research carried out today would not be unfamiliar to John Frere and his mid 19th century successors Charles Lyell, Joseph Prestwich and John Evans. One obvious similarity is in the way in which new sites are detected. There can be little doubt that in Britain Palaeolithic archaeologists of today are just as reliant on aggregate extraction for the discovery of artefacts as their 19th century forebears. Only very rarely do surface traces of human activities left from such distant times survive in circumstances that allow

their discovery by conventional archaeological survey. In this way at least Palaeolithic archaeology of the 2000s is every bit as reactive to external factors as it was a century ago. Indeed the adoption of mechanised sorting of sands and gravels during the 1920s and 1930s may have caused a reduction in the number of new finds being made, suggesting that recovery in the 19th and early 20th centuries was more thorough than at the present day (Roe 1981; Hosfield 1999). Perhaps this is one reason why a large proportion of excavation reports published in the last decade and relating to the Lower Palaeolithic are of sites originally found prior to the second world war, e.g. Barnham (Ashton, Lewis & Parfitt 1998), Hoxne (Singer, Gladfelter & Wymer 1993) and Swanscombe (Conway, McNabb & Ashton 1996).

Given the situation outlined above, this paper explores ways in which today's archaeologists working on the Lower Palaeolithic (this term is used for the entire Palaeolithic preceding 40,000 BP, following Wymer 1999: 2) might alleviate some of the restrictions imposed by the current database. Key amongst these is the need for renewed archaeological prospection of Pleistocene deposits, an activity which has hitherto been seen as looking for the proverbial needle in the haystack and has very rarely been undertaken. Arguably the location and subsequent investigation of new sites through prospection designed to an archaeological agenda is more likely to produce data relevant to current research questions concerning social behaviour of middle Pleistocene hominids (Gamble 1999), as well as enhancing traditional typological and technological studies. Given the forum in which this paper is presented, the examples used are taken wherever possible from central southern England, but the arguments are more widely applicable to southern England as a whole.

THE EXISTING BRITISH LOWER PALAEOLITHIC 'DATABASE'

Nature of the Lower Palaeolithic record

Students of the English Palaeolithic are fortunate in that a full record of Lower Palaeolithic artefact find-spots has been integrated as a single database by the Southern Rivers Palaeolithic Project (SRPP) and the English Rivers Palaeolithic survey (TERPS) (Wymer 1996, 1999). This work, which has significantly built on Roe's earlier gazetteer (Roe 1968), demonstrates that the vast majority of recorded artefacts have been found in reworked contexts, and these mainly in river gravels relating to cold stages of the Pleistocene (Wymer 1999: 21). In contrast sites where evidence of human activity survives *in situ* are correspondingly rare, and as discussed below are largely confined to relatively unusual geological circumstances. Detailed work has been carried out on many of the reworked artefact assemblages both at the level of the individual site (e.g. Dunbridge in the Test Valley (Bridgland & Harding 1993; Harding 1998)) and to explore regional patterns of hominid exploitation (Hosfield 1999). As reworked artefacts are thought to represent a reasonably representative sample of human activity over long periods of time their study has enabled conclusions to be drawn about changing technologies (Roe 1981, this volume) and raw material use (MacRae & Moloney 1988; MacRae 1989; White 1996). The data has been taken one interpretative step further by Hosfield (1999) in an attempt to reconstruct Palaeolithic demography, and results have suggested southern Britain may have been occupied for as little as 3.5% of the 'open landscape phases' of the Middle Pleistocene.

Problems with existing data

As discussed in the introduction it is arguable that the present data, even if collected as painstakingly as

was the case with the SRPP and TERPS, is adequate for addressing the questions posed by today's archaeologists. In no small part this is due to bias in the existing database and the chance nature of archaeological discovery (Roe 1996). Unlike Holocene archaeology, almost all Lower Palaeolithic sites found in England have been found by chance, usually as the result of a worker, or a passing antiquarian/archaeologist noting objects of interest in gravel pits. This is the case for famous sites such as Swanscombe, Hoxne and Boxgrove, just as much as for findspots of single handaxes or flakes. Aggregates tend to be exploited where they are of high quality, and/or strategically placed in relation to demand, while antiquarian activity is largely confined to certain areas of southern England (Hosfield 1999). These are undoubtedly contributing factors to the apparent clusters in Roe's (1964) and Wymer's (1999) distribution maps, in the Thames valley, southern Hampshire and central East Anglia. It is possible that the clusters may also be a result of the impact of publicised discoveries promoting intense collection within the surrounding area, resulting in further artefacts being recovered, a sort of snowball effect. Indeed Hosfield (1999) has modelled 'collector behaviour', amongst a number of other variables relating to site discovery and suggests that each collector may have operated within a territory of 40km radius, with a reduction in coverage towards the edge of the range. Within these collection areas concentrations of artefacts are recorded in the site distribution maps. As has previously been discussed it is also notable that less artefacts and few new sites have been discovered following the abandonment of manual gravel extraction and sorting in the early part of the 20th century, meaning that the site distribution maps of today are largely 'fossils' of the 1930s and earlier. While the statistical modelling approaches adopted by Hosfield can be employed to 'allow' for bias of this type for locations where artefacts have been found, it is less help in those areas where the site distribution maps are blank. Whether these areas really represent locations where there was no activity in the Lower Palaeolithic, or whether it is simply the case that nobody has looked is unclear on the basis of present data. Recent discoveries of handaxes from within a channel at Latton, Cirencester, several kilometres from the nearest known findspot (S. Lewis pers. comm.), suggest that the latter is at least partly the case.

Reliance on discoveries made during the 19th and early 20th centuries occasionally causes problems on an altogether different level, that of provenance. While artefacts recovered in this period can often be related to individual quarries, and hence to a spatial locality, they can less frequently be related to a given bed. Indeed large sections of some recent published accounts are given over to detailed studies of degrees of weathering, patination, colour and even microfossil

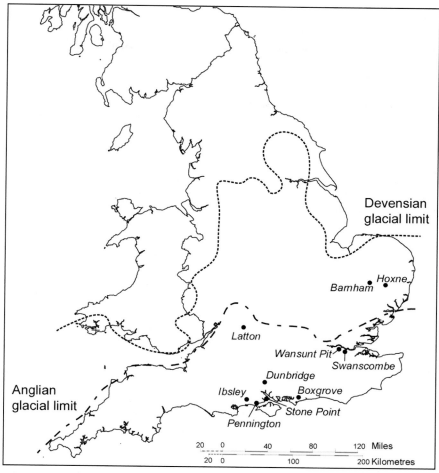

Figure 10.1: location of sites referred to in the text and the area relevant to this paper as defined by the southern margins of Devensian glacier ice

content of mud attached to artefacts, just to attribute an artefact to a given bed. Uncertainties of provenance are particularly significant when deposits in a quarry relate to a number of different chronological stages, as is the case with some fluvial gravel extraction pits (Bridgland 1995). Recent models of terrace chronology for rivers in southern England partly rely in changes in artefact typology in different geological units (Bridgland 1994, 1996, this volume). Therefore from the point of view of confidence when correlating gravel body with artefact 'inclusions' and hence age, it is vitally important that the finds are provenanced accurately. That this cannot be achieved where recent work has not been carried out restricts the application of this 'typological' dating of Pleistocene deposits.

To summarise, the Lower Palaeolithic database is in no small part a product of factors beyond the control of archaeologists. While not in itself a problem there are inherent implications for the way that archaeologists use the data to generate models. Given the difficulties with the existing record, dedicated prospection for Palaeolithic sites might recover more representative data, could also be targeted at the discovery of certain types of site and

might be formulated to address specific research questions, for example obtaining evidence for the presence/absence/nature of group interaction (Gamble 1996, 1999).

Solutions: prospecting for Palaeolithic sites

It is all very well stating that prospection should take place, but it is quite another to formulate an appropriate strategy. Unlike much Holocene archaeology Lower Palaeolithic sites are typically deeply buried, which when combined with the fact that they are not associated with obvious archaeological features/structures make them both technically difficult and expensive to investigate. However, one possible avenue for prospection which can partially circumnavigate these problems is through the planning process, of which archaeology has been considered an intrinsic part since 1990 (Department of the Environment 1990). Any scheme that requires planning consent can now have an archaeological 'condition' placed upon it by a local planning authority, allowing archaeologists to work on a site before and during development. These might include infrastructure schemes (which when of large enough scale also legally require detailed Environmental Impact Assessments), pipelines, housing as well as aggregate extraction; all of which may impact Pleistocene deposits. Such schemes occur throughout the country and thus although biases of distribution do occur they are not as marked as those effecting the location of 19th and early 20th century quarries, or antiquarians territories. Similarly with improvements in transport in the latter part of the 20th century aggregate quarries can be located at greater distances from their markets and thus are less concentrated around major conurbations (Hosfield 1999). Therefore in theory the investigation of such sites using modern archaeological techniques would allow the collection of representative data relating to the Lower Palaeolithic period.

THE PLANNING PROCESS AND LOWER PALAEOLITHIC ARCHAEOLOGY

British planning regulations are now among the most archaeologically-friendly of those found anywhere in the world, in no small part as the result of the publication of Planning Policy Guidance 16 (PPG 16) in November 1990 (Department of the Environment 1990). This measure established the principal whereby developers have to pay for archaeological survey (which might include desk top study and field evaluation) and subsequent mitigation (for example a watching brief, excavation or preservation of the site *in situ*) should their works impact on significant archaeological remains. Archaeologists in local planning departments ('curators') are charged with implementing PPG 16 and base decisions largely on whether a site scheduled for development contains, or is adjacent to known archaeological sites. The latter information is contained within the Sites and Monuments Record (SMR), and in the case of the Lower Palaeolithic is largely informed by SRPP and TERPS data. However, curators can also ask for investigations even when there are no sites listed on the SMR, but where data from other locales suggests that significant archaeology might be present. As might be expected this flexibility means that investigation of the Lower Palaeolithic as part of the planning process is patchy, largely as a result of variations in perceived importance and knowledge of curators of Palaeolithic archaeology. In general those areas (such as Hampshire and West Sussex) where SRPP and TERPS have demonstrated large numbers of sites have a greater awareness of matters Palaeolithic, and therefore have a sympathetic view to prospection for sites of this period through PPG 16. However, in other areas Pleistocene deposits found at the base of Holocene stratigraphy are considered to be 'the natural', and the point at which archaeological

investigation stops! Sites in the latter areas may well have been lost without record given the problems of currently available site distribution data and hence representation on SMR's. The variability in approach is being addressed through documents such as English Heritage's (1998) *Identifying and protecting Palaeolithic remains: archaeological guidance for planning authorities and developers* and in training programmes. Assuming this process succeeds it will be possible to prospect for Palaeolithic sites wherever a development intrudes into relevant Pleistocene deposits. However, in order for an investigation to move beyond the desktop survey the likelihood of important archaeological remains being found on the site must be demonstrated.

'VALUE' IN THE PALAEOLITHIC RECORD

The key word in the previous sentence is 'importance' or as is more commonly stated within the English Heritage literature, 'value'. While there is no doubt that every archaeological find of Palaeolithic date has some importance, some sites are obviously more important than others. Whether value judgements of this nature — which of course are largely subjective and may alter with changes of research interest — should be made at all is in theory questionable. Nevertheless for reasons of pragmatics, judgements have to be made simply because there is only so much money that can be spent on archaeology and thus the investigation of every findspot in the minutest detail cannot be funded. Questions of value are particularly important to curators who must justify any archaeological work they ask for prior to development. While this may be relatively easy for the feature-based archaeology of the late Prehistoric and historic periods, it is much more difficult for the ephemeral sites characterising the Palaeolithic.

Assuming that it is desirable to 'rank' in some way the relative importance of different types of site, how might this be done? The most obvious division of sites presently known from the British Lower Palaeolithic is into those where original activity areas have been preserved intact (*in situ*) and those where vestiges of human action have been removed and re-deposited elsewhere (derived). The SRPP and TERPS (Wymer 1999) overwhelmingly suggest that the latter dominate the record. The difficulties of interpreting derived artefact assemblages have in part already been discussed. Nevertheless it is data of this sort that is used as a proxy for long term processes operating at large spatial scales such as technological change, colonisation and demographic patterning. As demonstrated by Hosfield's (1999, this volume) study of the Hampshire basin, in order for these questions to be addressed with any degree of confidence large quantities of data (i.e. find-spots) are needed. In contrast *in situ* sites in the British Lower Palaeolithic can represent only minutes of human activity, yet a detailed picture of those actions can be reconstructed from evidence left in those brief moments. Even a single *in situ* activity area can contribute highly significant new information. Witness for example the earliest British evidence of hunting (as opposed to scavenging) from the Boxgrove horse kill (Pitts & Roberts 1997). Gamble (1996; 1999: 67–97) sees the two types of British Lower Palaeolithic data as complementary and that by 'tacking' between them questions asked at several spatial and temporal scales can be addressed. However, it can be argued that any future concentration on 'tacking' towards long time frame and large spatial scale investigation using reworked artefacts as a proxy must be subject to the law of diminishing returns. A huge quantity of new data would be required in order to say anything significantly new, except to extend distributions beyond currently recognised margins (Roe 1996). It can also be argued that the location of reworked artefacts is largely known (Middle Pleistocene river terraces in southern and eastern England) and that to investigate them by excavation or even field evaluation is clearly unrealistic (terraces are vertically and laterally extensive, while derived artefacts within them will have little meaningful spatial patterning).

In contrast activity areas preserved *in situ* have a significance beyond that of the single data point. Finds from Boxgrove for example provide information on the minutiae of tool production and use, the interactions of hominids with their environment and even the mechanics of group activity (Gamble 1999: 152). Data of this nature stands on its own irrespective of whether another 10 Boxgrove-type sites are found. Indeed the relative paucity of *in situ* sites in the British Lower Palaeolithic record means that those few that are known take on greater significance than they should, and come to be thought of as 'representative' of hominid activity for periods of 10's of thousands of years or more. The need to prospect for further sites that have been preserved *in situ* is thus clear in order to extend the narrative of the British Lower Palaeolithic, but is also of vital importance to stop the loss of such sites without record as the result of development. Fortunately conditions where *in situ* remains are preserved can in the case of southern England, be predicted geologically. The relevant deposits are much less extensive than the gravel terraces previously discussed, representing instead areas that could relatively easily be investigated as part of any development. In their advice document to curators English Heritage (1998) lay out criteria which may be used to assess the value of a Palaeolithic site (Table 10.1). While it is unclear whether the criteria are in priority order they nevertheless indicate the relative significance of *in situ* and reworked assemblages, and it is the former that are given priority.

LOCATING *IN SITU* PALAEOLITHIC ACTIVITY AREAS

Depositional environments of the British Pleistocene

The arguments rehearsed in the previous section indicate that for both pragmatic reasons and those of research interest, prospection for Lower Palaeolithic sites as part of PPG16 should be focussed on locating *in situ* remains of hominid activity areas. Sites of this nature are only likely to be located on former Pleistocene terrestrial surfaces, the remnants of which survive in a limited number of depositional environments. These terrestrial surfaces were occasionally stable enough for soils to develop — an example being Boxgrove where the activity areas occurred on the surface of an immature soil (Macphail 1999) — but the associated sediment frequently contain no evidence for pedogenesis. Nevertheless all such surfaces have one thing in common; they occur within or on top of fine grained deposits typical of the margins of depositional systems, as for example on river floodplains and in the intertidal zone. However, destructive processes — not least of which are glacial and periglacial processes operating during Pleistocene cold stages — have preferentially removed most of these deposits where they have not been protected by the rapid burial of coarser grained deposits. Nevertheless where they survive such sediments present an easily visible target for prospection, and can be considered as 'marker beds' for *in situ* Palaeolithic archaeology. Within southern Britain there are a number of situations where fine grained deposits of archaeological significance survive, but for reasons of space only two are examined here, namely former fluvial and coastal environments.

Coastal environments

Due to uplift of southern England during the Quaternary (Preece *et al.* 1990), coastlines relating to former high sea level events are preserved at elevations above Ordnance Datum, in various localities between Torquay and the Solent, but are continuous between Portsdown near Portsmouth and Brighton (Keen 1995). These interglacial raised beaches (coastlines of colder stages of the Pleistocene occur well below current sea-level) are likely to have formed in similar environments as present day marine margins. Many of the Pleistocene beaches are composed of sea-borne sands and gravels — for example beaches on the eastern side of Portland Bill deposited in Oxygen Isotope Stage (OIS) 5e (Davies & Keen 1985) — and are unlikely locations for Palaeolithic artefacts, whether *in situ* or not. However, as well as beaches deposited by high wave energies, high sea level events in the Pleistocene also

Criteria	Notes
• Any human bone is present in relevant deposits	▪ Only three Lower Palaeolithic sites in mainland Britain currently fulfil this criteria; Boxgrove, Swanscombe and Pontnewydd Cave
• The remains are in an undisturbed primary context	▪ By definition only relevant to *in situ* sites
• The remains belong to a period or geographic area where evidence of a human presence is particularly rare or was previously unknown	▪ In the case of the Lower Palaeolithic outside East Anglia, the Midlands and south-east England
• Organic (such as the wooden spear from Clacton-on-Sea) artefacts are present	▪ The Clacton spear is at present the only example of such a find in the Lower Palaeolithic of Britain
• Well-preserved indicators of the contemporary environment (floral, faunal, sedimentological etc) can be directly related to the remains	▪ Applicable to re-worked material in exceptional cases, but such environmental evidence is only truly contemporary if artefacts represent *in situ* activity
• There is evidence of lifestyle (such as interference with animal remains)	▪ Many sites now have evidence of human presence from cut-marked bone. These include fossils from the Cromer fresh waterbed which pre-dates human activity at Boxgrove and Westbury-sub-Mendip (Parfitt pers. comm.)
• One deposit containing Palaeolithic remains has a clear stratigraphic relationship with another	▪ Superimposition of Acheulian over Clactonian industries at Barnham and Swanscombe are good examples
• Any artistic representation, no matter how simple is present	▪ Only relevant to Upper Palaeolithic based on present evidence
• Any structure, such as a hearth, shelter, floor, securing device etc. survives	▪ No such remains are currently known with any certainty in Britain
• The site can be related to the exploitation of a resource, such as a raw material	▪ A good example is the use of flint nodules eroding out of the cliff face at Boxgrove
• Artefacts are abundant	▪ No definition of what 'abundant' means is provided. However, the 400+ handaxes from Dunbridge undoubtedly qualifies this site

Table 10.1: English Heritage (1998) criteria for identifying 'value' in the English Palaeolithic

deposited fine grained deposits in estuarine and barrier beach systems. On macrotidal coastlines characteristic of Britain today, and presumably also during the Pleistocene, fine grained deposits are found in laterally extensive tidal-flats, which are inundated by the sea during twice daily tidal cycles. Tidal flats have been extensively exploited for a variety of reasons by people during the Holocene (e.g. Bell, Caseldine & Neumann 2000), but Britain's most famous Palaeolithic site, Boxgrove is also associated with this depositional environment (Roberts 1986; Roberts *et al.* 1997; Roberts & Parfitt 1999). The artefacts, butchered animal remains and hominid bones were all deposited on an immature soil (Unit 4c) developing on tidal flats (Units 4a and 4b) (Collcutt 1999; Macphail 1999) as sea levels fell. Boxgrove is thus far unique, but it is highly likely that sites of similar nature occur in other raised beaches of the West Sussex coastal plain as well as elsewhere in the Goodwood–Slindon raised beach (Figure 10.2). Indeed artefacts recovered by antiquarians from the younger (OIS 7) Brighton–Norton raised beach hint that further sites might be found in this beach where fine grained deposits relating to sea-level falls also occur (Bates 1998a; Bates, Parfitt & Roberts 1998; Bates *et al.* 2000).

To date fine grained deposits of the Goodwood–Slindon and Brighton–Norton raised beaches have only been encountered in the immediate vicinity of former cliff lines (Roberts 1999a; Bates *et al.* 2000) and it would appear that these have protected the sediments from later erosion. Thus, although the distribution of fine grained sediments is restricted on a north-south axis to several 10's of metres, they are potentially extensive in an east to west direction. These properties make location of such high potential archaeological deposits prior to development relatively straightforward. Bore hole surveys can take place on north to south transects (Bates 1998b; Wilkinson 1999) to locate the deposits, and where these are found Wenner array resistivity survey carried out to better define deposit extents and cliff position (Lewis & Roberts 1999; Bates *et al.* 2000).

Locations where fine grained deposits and cliff lines are found can then be closely monitored during development by means of an intense watching brief combined with evaluation and excavation where needed.

Fluvial environments

As is obvious from both this contribution and others in the volume artefacts found from Pleistocene fluvial environments dominate the Lower Palaeolithic archaeological record. This is perhaps not surprising given the intense commercial exploitation of gravel terraces associated with these fluvial systems over the past two centuries, but is also likely to reflect the

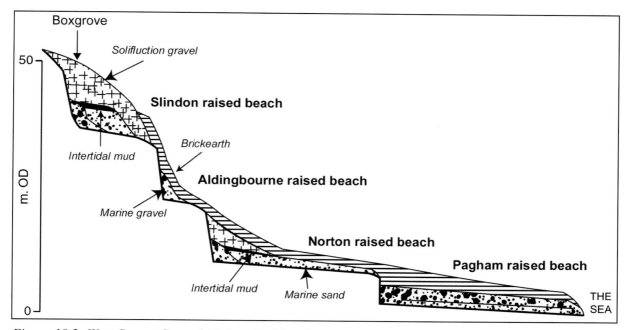

Figure 10.2: West Sussex Coastal Plain raised beach sequence (after Roberts & Parfitt 1999)

behaviour of Middle Pleistocene hominids. For example it has been argued on the basis of site distribution, particularly from that in areas away from south-eastern England, that Lower Palaeolithic people were exploiting the ecotonal environments of the floodplains in preference to the surrounding 'uplands' (Roe 1996; Wymer 1999). The terrace 'staircases' associated with England's lowland rivers provide a receptacle of Palaeolithic artefacts, while the latter can be related to an approximate chronology based on the age of the terrace (and vice-versa if changes in artefact typology with time are to be believed) (Bridgland 1996). These terraces do not uniformly consist of gravels; fine grained deposits frequently occur and are occasionally associated with *in situ* archaeology.

In recent years Bridgland (1994, 1995, this volume) has developed a model for the evolution of terrace sequences over glacial-interglacial timescales, a scheme that has been utilised by Wymer (1999: 25–29) to explain the incorporation of archaeological artefacts into associated deposits (Figure 10.3). The model suggests that most gravel accretion, and hence artefact reworking, took place during early and late glacial periods, phases 2 and 4 of Bridgland's (1995: Figure 7) model (Figure 10.3). It is possible that hominids were present in southern England during these cold episodes (although almost certainly not during the mid-glacials), but seem to have been particularly active during early and late stages of interglacials when conditions were relatively warm, but tree cover sparse (Gamble 1986; Stringer & Gamble 1993). Therefore the majority of artefacts will have originally been deposited on relatively stable floodplain surfaces that were forming during Bridgland's phase 3 (Figure 10.3), and were

subsequently either reworked, or buried *in situ* by phase 4 gravel aggradation. Interglacial floodplains of southern England can be reconstructed by analogy with those of present (Holocene) interglacial meandering rivers. Meandering rivers are thought to have evolved from braided systems, perhaps through intermediate anastamosing forms, as a result of changes in sediment supply and base levels in late glacial and early interglacial stages (Starkel 1994; Collins *et al.* 1996; Tebbens *et al.* 1999; Sidell *et al.* 2000). Their floodplains largely comprise undifferentiated fine grain sediments (primarily clays, silts and fine sands) that are deposited by the river following episodic flood events (Brown 1997). For the majority of the year the floodplains are relatively dry and available for human exploitation, yet the annual flood has the effect of inhibiting tree colonisation and hindering soil formation. This situation appears to be that in which hominids were active in the lower Thames in OIS 11, as represented for example by *in situ* artefact scatters in the Lower loam at Swanscombe (Bridgland 1994; Ashton, McNabb & Bridgland 1995; Conway, McNabb & Ashton 1996) and the Wansunt loam, Wansunt Pit (White *et al.* 1995; pers. comm.). Fine grained deposits are also found on Holocene floodplains associated with fills of cut off meanders, but hominid activity is only likely to have taken place on the margins of such features given that they will have been filled with water for much of the year.

Floodplain fines are rare in the Pleistocene record away from lower reaches of the Thames, probably as a result of near complete reworking during Bridgland's (1995: Figure 7), phase 4 terrace development in other rivers. For example in the Solent system, which appears similar to the

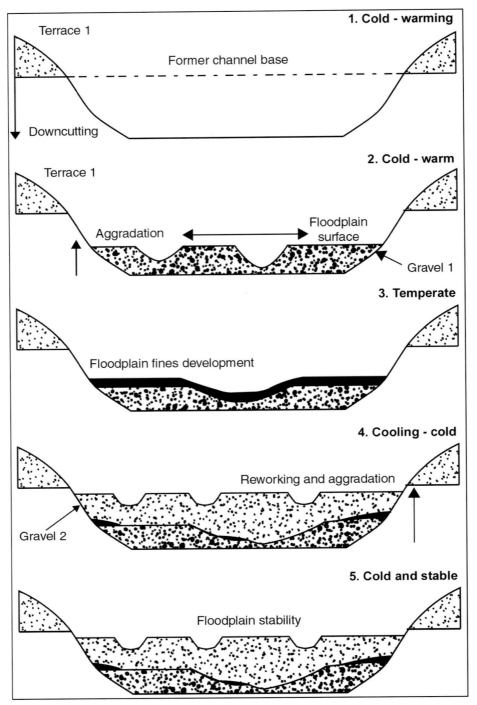

Figure 10.3: Bridgland's (1994, 1995, 1996) model of fluvial terrace development over a single glacial/interglacial cycle

Pleistocene Thames in many respects, such deposits are known only from Stone Point, Lepe (West & Sparks 1960; Green & Keen 1987; Reynolds & Catt 1987), Pennington Marshes, Lymington (Allen, Preece & Robinson 1996) and Ibsley, near Ringwood (Barber & Brown 1987) and date either to OIS 7 or OIS 5e. As Pleistocene fine-grained deposits in most river systems are found in restricted distributions the sort of bore hole surveys suggested for coastal plain studies are in most cases inappropriate — a negative result would provide no confidence of a real absence of such deposits. Therefore although most river terraces offer some potential for containing fine grained deposits, little in the way of pre-development survey can be carried out except to place the deposits being removed within existing stratigraphy and chronological frameworks. Given the apparent absence of hominids from Britain from the middle of OIS 6 to OIS 3 (Gamble 1986; Sutcliffe 1995; Barton 1997) the latter is particularly important as *in situ* archaeological materials are unlikely to occur in deposits of this period – although of course 'gaps' in the archaeological record can be proven incorrect by just one find! Watching briefs undertaken while Pleistocene fluvial deposits are removed allow opportunities to observe ephemeral fine grained beds and assess their archaeological potential. Visits made to a quarry at regular intervals as the working face changes, not only allow fine grained deposits to be recorded, but also enable sections and reject piles to be checked for reworked artefacts – as for example has been taking place since 1991 at Dunbridge near Romsey (Bridgland & Harding 1993; Harding 1998). Where intrusion into Pleistocene deposits is not for aggregate exploitation, which may for example occur during the construction of a pipeline, a watching brief may have to be more flexibly arranged, so that visits can be made as new areas are worked. Whatever watching brief arrangements are made the importance of clauses in contracts to stop extraction/development should important finds be made is vital, as is contingency finance to fund associated analytical work. Unfortunately investigations of this nature are at present only ordered in areas where dense concentrations of artefacts have previously been found, a state of affairs that only reinforces the patterns of present site distribution maps.

CONCLUSIONS

Research on the Lower Palaeolithic is now entering a third century and those involved are at a crossroads. Should the British Palaeolithic community continue to work within the confines of the existing data as detailed by the SRPP and TERPS, or should researchers reclaim the initiative to better address research questions through new data? Arguably the latter is preferable, as without new sites British Palaeolithic studies will inevitably stagnate through the restricted size of the database – a site yields progressively less further information the more it is investigated. Indeed an implicit aim of the SRPP and TERPS was to set the existing data 'in stone' and act as a stimulus for further discovery (Wymer 1999: 193–196). The only way to increase the present database is to prospect, but for a period separated from the present by numerous millennia, and from modern ground surfaces by metres of sediment, this is infinitely easier to say than to do. Nevertheless the nature of the present planning legislation and better awareness of curators is allowing just this type of survey to be undertaken. What is now questioned in many areas of southern England is not whether prospection should be carried out, but rather what should be looked for and the methodology to be employed. It is true that prospections carried out in this way suffer from certain biases in relation to location and brief, but arguably these are of less

severity than those imposed on the current record by, amongst others, aggregate extraction policy in the 19th/early 20th centuries and the nature of antiquarian perambulation. Investigations as part of the planning process also have the advantage of being relatively well funded as a result of the 'polluter pays' principle inherent in PPG 16 (Department of the Environment 1990). Furthermore if such projects are carried out with an attention to public and developer interest, they have the beneficial side effect of actively promoting interest in the Palaeolithic period to a wider audience, something which can only be of benefit to all working in the subject.

The paper has highlighted mechanisms by which prospection can be carried out in just two depositional environments, but of course methodologies need to be developed for loessic and even periglacial sediments, within which discoveries on the mainland of Europe have indicated that important archaeological sites may be buried. Similarly the author does not seek to dismiss 'reworked' artefacts from prospection strategies, but rather suggests that their recovery can only remain as part of mitigation during development rather than investigation beforehand. Despite these caveats it is unlikely that all will agree with the sentiments expressed in the preceding text. However, in light of the increased awareness of the Palaeolithic amongst the whole archaeological community and in particular by those 'managing' the 'archaeological resource', now is the time to debate mechanisms by which new data can be collected and how it is subsequently used.

ACKNOWLEDGMENTS

An initial version of this paper was presented at a seminar of the Human Origins Research Group, University of Southampton and I would like to thank all who attended for a stimulating debate, much of which has been translated into the preceding text. I also acknowledge Hampshire County Council, who through the good offices of David Hopkins and Ian Wykes, have both helped fund and provided unpublished information, that have aided research on Palaeolithic Hampshire at King Alfred's College. Finally I would like to express my gratitude to Dr Mark White (University of Durham) for providing unpublished data relating to the site of Wansunt Pit, Dartford and Dr Simon Lewis (Queen Mary College, University of London) for data from Latton, Wiltshire. I need hardly add that the views expressed in this paper are entirely my own and do not represent the policy of any organisation.

REFERENCES

Allen, L., Preece, R.C. & Robinson, J.E. 1996. Late Pleistocene interglacial deposits at Pennington Marshes, Lymington, Hampshire, England. *Proceedings of the Geologists' Association* 107: 39–50.

Ashton, N., McNabb, J. & Bridgland, D.R. 1995. Barnfield Pit, Swanscombe (TQ 598743). In D.R. Bridgland, P. Allen & B.A. Haggart (ed's) *The Quaternary of the Lower Reaches of the Thames*: 129–141. Quaternary Research Association, Durham.

Ashton, N., Lewis, S.G. & Parfitt, S.A. 1998. *Excavations at the Lower Palaeolithic site at East Farm, Barnham, Suffolk 1989–1994*. British Museum Occasional Paper 125. British Museum, London.

Barber, K.E. & Brown, A.G. 1987. Late Pleistocene organic deposits beneath the floodplain of the river Avon, Ibsley, Hampshire. In K.E. Barber (ed.) *Wessex and the Isle of Wight: Field guide*: 65–74. Quaternary Research Association, Cambridge.

Barton, R.N.E. 1997. *Stone Age Britain*. English Heritage, London.

Bates, M.R. 1998a. Pleistocene deposits at Portfield Pit, Westhampnett East, Chichester. In J.B. Murton, C.A. Whiteman, M.R. Bates, D.R. Bridgland, A.J. Long, M.B. Roberts & M.P. Waller (ed's) *The Quaternary of Kent and Sussex: Field guide*: 175–186. Quaternary Research Association, London.

Bates, M.R. 1998b. Pleistocene sequences at Norton Farm, Chichester, West Sussex. In J.B. Murton, C.A. Whiteman, M.R. Bates, D.R. Bridgland, A.J. Long, M.B. Roberts & M.P. Waller (ed's) *The Quaternary of Kent and Sussex: Field guide*: 168–176. Quaternary Research Association, London.

Bates, M.R., Bates, C.R., Gibbard, P.L., Macphail, R.I., Owen, F.J., Parfitt, S.A., Preece, R.C., Roberts, M.B., Robinson, J.E., Whittaker, J.E. & Wilkinson, K.N. 2000. Late Middle Pleistocene deposits at Norton Farm on the West Sussex coastal plain, southern England. *Journal of Quaternary Science* 15: 61–89.

Bates, M.R., Parfitt, S.A. & Roberts, M.B. 1998. Palaeolithic archaeology and Quaternary stratigraphy of the West Sussex coastal plain. In J.B. Murton, C.A. Whiteman, M.R. Bates, D.R. Bridgland, A.J. Long, M.B. Roberts & M.P. Waller (ed's) *The Quaternary of Kent and Sussex: Field guide*: 165–167. Quaternary Research Association, London.

Bell, M., Caseldine, A. & Neumann, H. 2000. *Prehistoric intertidal archaeology in the Welsh Severn Estuary*. Council for British Archaeology Research Report 120. Council for British Archaeology, York.

Bowen, D.Q. (ed.). 1999. *A revised correlation of Quaternary deposits in the British Isles*. The Geological Society Special Report 23. Geological Society, Bath.

Bridgland, D.R. 1994. *Quaternary of the Thames*. Chapman and Hall, London.

Bridgland, D.R. 1995. The Quaternary sequence of the eastern Thames basin: problems of correlation. In D.R. Bridgland, P. Allen & B.A. Haggart (ed's) *The Quaternary of the Lower Reaches of the Thames*: 35–52. Quaternary Research Association, Durham.

Bridgland, D.R. 1996. Quaternary river terrace deposits as a framework for the Lower Palaeolithic record. In C.S. Gamble & A.J. Lawson (ed's) *The English Palaeolithic Reviewed*: 24–39. Trust for Wessex Archaeology, Salisbury.

Bridgland, D.R. & Harding, P.A. 1993. Preliminary observations at the Kimbridge Farm quarry, Dunbridge, Hampshire: early results of a watching brief. *Quaternary Newsletter* 69: 1–9.

Brown, A.G. 1997. *Alluvial geoarchaeology: floodplain archaeology and environmental change*. Cambridge University Press, Cambridge.

Collcutt, S.N. 1999. Structural sedimentology at Boxgrove. In M.B. Roberts & S.A. Parfitt (ed's) *Boxgrove: a Middle Pleistocene hominid site at Eartham Quarry, Boxgrove, West Sussex*: 42–99. English Heritage, London.

Collins, P.E.F., Fenwick, I.M., Keith-Lucas, D.M. & Worsley, P. 1996. Late Devensian river and floodplain dynamics and related environmental change in northwest Europe, with particular reference to a site at Woolhampton, Berkshire, England. *Journal of Quaternary Science* 11: 257–375.

Conway, B., McNabb, J. & Ashton, N. 1996. *Excavations at Barnfield Pit, Swanscombe 1968–72*. British Museum Press, London.

Davies, K.H. & Keen, D.H. 1985. The age of the Pleistocene marine deposits at Portland, Dorset. *Proceedings of the Geologists' Association* 96: 217–225.

Department of the Environment. 1990. *Archaeology and planning*. Department of the Environment Planning Policy Guidance Notes 16. HMSO, London.

English Heritage. 1998. *Identifying and protecting Palaeolithic remains: archaeological guidance for planning authorities and developers*. HMSO, London.

Frere, J. 1800. Account of flint weapons discovered at Hoxne in Suffolk, in a letter to the Rev. John Brand, Secretary. *Archaeologia* 13: 204–205.

Gamble, C.S. 1986. *The Palaeolithic Settlement of Europe*. Cambridge University Press, Cambridge.

Gamble, C.S. 1996. Hominid behaviour in the Middle Pleistocene: an English perspective. In C.S. Gamble & A.J. Lawson (ed's) *The English Palaeolithic Reviewed*: 63–71. Trust for Wessex Archaeology, Salisbury.

Gamble, C.S. 1999. *The Palaeolithic Societies of Europe*. Cambridge University Press, Cambridge.

Green, C.P. & Keen, D.H. 1987. Stratigraphy and palaeoenvironments of the Stone Point deposits: the 1975 investigation. In K.E. Barber (ed.) *Wessex and the Isle of Wight: Field guide*: 17–20. Quaternary Research Association, Cambridge.

Harding, P.A. 1998. An interim report of an archaeological watching brief on Palaeolithic deposits at Dunbridge, Hants. In N. Ashton, F. Healy & P. Pettitt (ed's) *Stone Age archaeology: Essays in honour of John Wymer*: 72–76. Oxbow Monograph 102 & Lithic Studies Society Occasional Paper 6. Oxbow, Oxford.

Hosfield, R. 1999. *The Palaeolithic of the Hampshire basin. A regional model of hominid behaviour during the Middle Pleistocene*. British Archaeological Reports British Series 286. Archaeopress, Oxford.

Keen, D.H. 1995. Raised beaches and sea-levels in the English Channel in the Middle and Late Pleistocene: problems of interpretation and implications for the isolation of the British Isles. In R.C. Preece (ed.) *Island Britain: a Quaternary perspective*: 63–74. Geological Society Special Publication 96. Geological Society, London.

Lewis, S.G. & Roberts, C.L. 1999. Location of the buried cliff-line using resistivity methods. In M.B. Roberts &

108

S.A. Parfitt (ed's) *Boxgrove: a Middle Pleistocene hominid site at Eartham Quarry, Boxgrove, West Sussex*: 37–42. English Heritage, London.

Macphail, R.I. 1999. Sediment micromorphology. In M.B. Roberts & S.A. Parfitt (ed's) *Boxgrove: a Middle Pleistocene hominid site at Eartham Quarry, Boxgrove, West Sussex*: 118–149. English Heritage, London.

MacRae, R.J. 1989. Belt, shoulder-bag or basket? An enquiry into handaxe transport and flint sources. *Lithics* 10: 2–8.

MacRae, R.J. & Moloney, N. 1988. *Non-flint stone tools and the Palaeolithic occupation of Britain*. British Archaeological Reports British Series 189. BAR, Oxford.

Pitts, M. & Roberts, M.B. 1997. *Fairweather Eden: life in Britain half a million years ago as revealed by excavations at Boxgrove*. Century, London.

Preece, R.C., Scourse, J.D., Houghton, S.D., Knudsen, K.L. & Penney, D.N. 1990. The Pleistocene sea-level and neotectonic history of the eastern Solent, southern England. *Philosophical Transactions of the Royal Society of London Series B328*: 425–477.

Reynolds, P.S. & Catt, J.A. 1987. Soils and vegetation history of abandoned enclosures in the New Forest, Hampshire, England. *Journal of Archaeological Science* 14: 507–527.

Roberts, M.B. 1986. Excavation of the lower Palaeolithic site at Amey's Eartham Pit, Boxgrove, West Sussex: a preliminary report. *Proceedings of the Prehistoric Society* 52: 215–245.

Roberts, M.B. 1999a. Geological framework. In M.B. Roberts & S.A. Parfitt (ed's) *Boxgrove: a Middle Pleistocene hominid site at Eartham Quarry, Boxgrove, West Sussex*: 21–37. English Heritage, London.

Roberts, M.B. 1999b. Project methodology. In M.B. Roberts & S.A. Parfitt (ed's) *Boxgrove: a Middle Pleistocene hominid site at Eartham Quarry, Boxgrove, West Sussex*: 15–19. English Heritage, London.

Roberts, M.B. & Parfitt, S.A. 1999. *Boxgrove: a Middle Pleistocene hominid site at Eartham Quarry, Boxgrove, West Sussex*. English Heritage, London.

Roberts, M.B., Parfitt, S.A., Pope, M.I. & F.F. Wenban-Smith. 1997. Boxgrove, West Sussex: rescue excavations of a Lower Palaeolithic land surface (Boxgrove Project B, 1989–91). *Proceedings of the Prehistoric Society* 63: 303–358.

Roe, D.A. 1964. The British Lower and Middle Palaeolithic: some problems, methods of study and preliminary results. *Proceedings of the Prehistoric Society* 30: 245–267.

Roe, D.A. 1968. *A gazetteer of British Lower and Middle Palaeolithic sites*. Council for British Archaeology Research Report 8. Council for British Archaeology, London.

Roe, D.A. 1981. *The Lower and Middle Palaeolithic periods in Britain*. Routledge and Kegan Paul, London.

Roe, D.A. 1996. Artefact distributions and the British earlier Palaeolithic. In C.S. Gamble & A.J. Lawson (ed's) *The English Palaeolithic reviewed*: 1–6. Trust for Wessex Archaeology, Salisbury.

Sidell, E.J., Wilkinson, K.N., Scaife, R.G. & Cameron, N. 2000. *The Holocene evolution of the London Thames*. Museum of London Archaeology Service Monograph 5, Museum of London Archaeology Service, London.

Singer, R., Gladfelter, B.G. & Wymer, J.J. 1993. *The Lower Paleolithic site at Hoxne, England*. University of Chicago Press, Chicago.

Starkel, L. 1994. Reflection of the glacial-interglacial cycle in the evolution of the Vistula river basin, Poland. *Terra Nova* 6: 486–494.

Stringer, C. & Gamble, C.S. 1993. *In search of the Neanderthals: solving the puzzle of human origins*. Thames and Hudson, London.

Sutcliffe, A.J. 1995. Insularity of the British Isles 250,000–30,000 years ago: the mammalian, including human, evidence. In R.C. Preece (ed.) *Island Britain: a Quaternary perspective*: 127–140. The Geological Society, London.

Tebbens, L.A., Veldkamp, A., Westerhoff, W. & Kroonenberg, S.B. 1999. Fluvial incision and channel downcutting as a response to Late-glacial and Early Holocene climate change: the lower reach of the River Meuse (Maas), The Netherlands. *Journal of Quaternary Science* 14: 59–76.

West, R.G. & Sparks, B.W. 1960. Coastal interglacial deposits of the English Channel. *Philosophical Transactions of the Royal Society of London Series B243*: 95–133.

White, M.J. 1996. Raw materials and biface variability in Southern Britain: a preliminary examination. *Lithics* 16: 1–20.

White, M., Bridgland, D.R., Ashton, N.M., McNabb, J. & Berger, M.A. 1995. Wansunt Pit, Dartford Heath (TQ 513737). In D.R. Bridgland, P. Allen & B.A. Haggart (ed's) *The Quaternary of the lower reaches of the Thames*: 117–128. Quaternary Research Association, Durham.

Wilkinson, K.N. 1999. *Drayton Lane, Oving: a geoarchaeological evaluation of Pleistocene strata*. Unpublished Report, King Alfred's College, Winchester.

Wymer, J.J. 1996. The English Rivers Palaeolithic Survey. In C.S. Gamble & A.J. Lawson (ed's) *The English Palaeolithic reviewed*: 7–23. Trust for Wessex Archaeology, Salisbury.

Wymer, J.J. 1999. *The Lower Palaeolithic occupation of Britain*. Wessex Archaeology and English Heritage, Salisbury.

SITE AND FIND-SPOT INDEX

Fareham, 40 Blackbrook Park Avenue, 55
Arago, 59
Ashford, 4
Baker's Farm, 52
Barnfield Pit, 49
Barnham, 49, 99, 104
Barton Cliffs, 18
Barton-on-Sea, 4
Bembridge, 3
Bleak Down, 71–72
Bouldnor Cliff, 13
Boxgrove, 17–18, 23, 30, 35, 41, 48, 50, 57–61, 67, 100, 103–104
Broom, 5, 55, 77–79, 81, 83
Cams Bridge, 39, 41
Cams Hall, 41
Canford, 17
Castle Lane, Moordown, 55
Chard Junction, 78, 83
Clacton, 49, 104
Corfe Mullen, 17, 49–50, 91
Crayford, 17
Cromer, 104
Cuxton, 52
Dartford Heath, 18
Down Coppice, 39
Down Coppice Gravel Pit, 36, 41
Downend Chalk Pit, 39
Downton, 4
Dunbridge, 4–5, 85–86, 88, 90–91, 100, 104, 107
Fort Wallington, 39
Furze Platt, 52
Great Pan Farm, 55, 71–72
Grotte Vaufrey, 59
Hawkchurch, 78
High Lodge, 17, 57–58, 67
Highfield, 57–58, 61, 67
Highfield Brick Pit, 62
Highfield Church, 52, 62
Highfield Church Pit, 63
Highlands Farm, 49
Highlands Farm Pit, 49
Hillhead, 4
Holditch Lane, 79–81, 83
Holditch Lane pits, 77–78
Hoxne, 57–58, 60, 67, 99–100

Ibsley, 19, 31, 106
Kent's Cavern, 50
Kimbridge, 88
Kimbridge Farm, 87–88
King's Park, Boscombe, 17
Latton, 100
Lion Point, Clacton, 49
Moreton, 17
Norton Farm, 30, 35, 41
Old Ballast Pit, 77–81, 83
Old Shirley, 52
Pennington, 31
Pennington Marshes, 19, 106
Pokesdown, 17
Pontnewydd Cave, 104
Portfield Pit, Westhampnett East, 31
Portland Bill, 103
Pratt's Old Pit, 78
Priory Bay, 3, 5, 71–75
Purfleet, 17
Pye Corner, 83
Queen's Park, Boscombe, 17
Railway Pit, 78
Rainbow Bar, 4, 47, 49
Red Barns, 4, 48, 52, 57–61
Redhill Common, 17
Rickson's Pit, 49
Selsey Bill, 29–30
Shirley Church, 52
Southampton, 61
Southbourne Broadway, 55
Stone Point, 19, 23, 106
Stone Point, Lepe, 31
Swanscombe, 18, 49, 59–60, 99–100, 104–105
Test Road Materials Pit, 52
Thorncombe, 78
Thurrock, 49
Wansunt Pit, 105
Warren Hill, 49
Warsash, 52, 61, 81
Westbury-sub-Mendip, 17, 104
Winton, 52
Wolvercote, 59, 60
Wolvercote Channel, 52
Wood Green, 5, 85–86, 88, 90–91

LITHIC STUDIES SOCIETY

The Lithic Studies Society, founded in 1979, seeks to advance the international study of lithic industries in the broadest possible context. The Society:

• holds regular lectures, day meetings, conferences, field trips and site visits — usually including opportunities to view and handle artefacts

• publishes an annual journal *Lithics* containing articles, book reviews and news of the Society's activities

• publishes conference proceedings and lithic-oriented thematic volumes as occasional papers of the Society

• promotes the highest standards of lithics research and reporting, and recognition of the role of lithics in broader studies of the past

• provides a convivial forum for the exchange of ideas and information

• maintains a regularly updated web-site (www.britarch.ac.uk/lithics/)

MEMBERSHIP
The Society has over 250 members from across the world. The Society is open to all who have, or would like to develop, an interest in lithic artefacts of any period and related matters. We are always delighted to welcome new members. The membership year runs from 1 Oct to 30 Sep, and the journal Lithics is published early the following year. Members receive:

• annual journal *Lithics*
• participation in day meetings, lectures, field trips and site visits
• Society publications at reduced prices

If you are interested in joining the Society, please fill out the application form below and return it to: LSS Hon. Treasurer and Membership Secretary, c/o British Museum (Quaternary Section), Franks House, 38–46 Orsman Road, London N1 5 QJ.

APPLICATION FORM

Title and name..

Address..

....

.... Postcode ....

I should like to join the Lithic Studies Society at the individual rate of £10 per annum.

* I enclose a cheque or bank draft for £10 (payable to the Lithic Studies Society, and drawn in pounds sterling on a UK bank account)

or (*Delete as applicable)

* I would like to pay by standing order (please complete the form below)

To the manager .... Bank

Branch address..

....

.... Postcode ....

Name (account holder) ....

Account number ....

I/we, the above-named account holder/s, instruct you to pay to the Lithic Studies Society (account 32164203) at the National Westminster Bank, George St, Edinburgh (sort-code 60-30-20) the sum of £10 immediately and the sum of £10 annually thereafter on 1 October, quoting the reference .... [your name] until otherwise instructed by myself/ourselves.

Signed .... Date ....

 # LITHIC STUDIES SOCIETY

OTHER PUBLICATIONS

Occasional papers

No. 3 *The Illustration of Lithic Artefacts: a Guide to Drawing Stone Tools for Specialist Reports.* H. Martingell & A. Saville (1988)

No. 4 *Stories in Stone: Proceedings of Anniversary Conference at St. Hilda's College, Oxford, April 1993.* N. Ashton & A. David, ed's (1994)

No. 5 *Lithics in Context: Suggestions for the Future Direction of Lithic Studies.* A.J. Schofield, ed. (1995)

No. 6 *Stone Age Archaeology: Essays in Honour of John Wymer.* N. Ashton, F. Healy & P. Pettitt, ed's (1998)

Lithics

Back issues of the Lithic Studies Society journal *Lithics*; various no.'s, including (at the time of going to press):

5	1984
6	1985
7	1986
8	1987
19	1998
20	1999
21	2000

Check with editor or web-site for current availability

Available from

The Association of Archaeological Illustrators
c/o Dept. Archaeology, Laver Building
University of Exeter, North Park Rd
Exeter EX4 4QE
[aais@exeter.ac.uk]

N. Ashton
British Museum (Quaternary Section)
Franks House, 38–46 Orsman Road
London N1 5 QJ
[nashton@british-museum.ac.uk]

Oxbow Books, Park End Place
Oxford OX1 1HN
[01865-241 249]

Oxbow Books, Park End Place
Oxford OX1 1HN
[01865-241 249]

M.J. White, Hon. Editor LSS
Dept. of Archaeology
University of Durham
South Road, Durham DH1 3LE
[m.j.white@durham.ac.uk]
[www.britarch.ac.uk/lithics/]